Implementing Lean Manufacturing Techniques

Making Your System Lean and Living With It

By
Julian Page

Library of Congress Cataloging-in-Publication Data

Page, Julian.
  Implementing lean manufacturing techniques / Julian Page.
     p. cm.
Includes index.
 1-56990-353-0
 1. Industrial management. I. Title.
 HD31.P2353 2003
 658.5'15—dc21

                                                        2003013826

While the advice and information in *Implementing Lean Manufacturing Techniques* are believed to be true, accurate, and reliable, neither the author nor the publisher can accept any legal responsibility for any errors, omissions, or damages that may arise out of the use of this advice and information. The author and publisher make no warranty of any kind, expressed or implied, with regard to the material contained in this work.

An ***Automotive Design and Production*** book published by
Gardner Publications
www.autofieldguide.com

Hanser Gardner Publications
6915 Valley Avenue
Cincinnati, OH 45244-3029
www.hansergardner.com

HANSER GARDNER
PUBLICATIONS

Contents

Foreword
By Dr. Jeff Liker

Too many companies kid themselves into believing they have lean operations. Admittedly, while there are probably a good number of companies making moves in the right direction, there are also many operations that "talk the talk" rather than "walk the walk." It is not that these companies do not understand what lean manufacturing is all about; but the fact remains that it sounds better to proclaim to be lean than to be otherwise.

When I use the term "lean," I am referring to reducing the timeline from customer order to building and to delivering a good quality product by eliminating waste. Lean must be recognized as a totally different way of manufacturing. Whereas traditional manufacturing approaches focus on wringing out a few minutes of efficiency here and there, lean manufacturing is about attacking waste—the massive areas in the value stream from raw material to finished goods, where no added value is taking place.

Another of the major problems with lean implementation has been an overload of *thought*, but too little planned, structured, and properly resourced *action*. It is like a funnel of lean know-how into which massive amounts of lean training, consulting, tools, speeches, seminars, books, and magazine articles have all been poured, yet what has come out of the spout has been only a tiny trickle.

In many operations, the time, energy, effort, and initiative necessary to make the actual and long-term changes have been applied to getting the product out the door. In addition, there has tended to be a cherry-picking mentality. Too many companies fall into the trap of mistaking lean thinking for lean tools and techniques, and simply using a method or two, or transforming one area of the plant.

But lean doesn't mean blindly applying kanban, going through the factory painting yellow lines everywhere, running individual Kaizen events, and so on. While this may provide short-term benefits, the real transformation comes from understanding and adopting the system of lean—a holistic system of manufacturing, and not a piecemeal approach.

Becoming lean, and staying that way, requires focus and commitment, and can take many years. For those managers whose time horizons do not stretch beyond weeks or months, this is a major stumbling block. But searching for a magic bullet is not the answer.

As anyone who has been on a diet will testify, there are no quick fixes—lean requires the same discipline and perseverance of trying to lose weight. Some people go from one diet plan to another, with the only constant being the return of excess weight. Those people who choose a sensible program—and maintain it—are the ones, in the long run, who lose the weight. And so it is with achieving lean manufacturing.

Far too many managers spend far too much time doing planning, analysis, training, and more planning. They don't actually do anything substantial to become lean. I know companies where the transition has taken ten years because the first five years were spent doing the "preparatory" work.

People must see change right away. The way to get started is through technical action, not interpersonal consensus. In other words, **move the machine**. But action is not enough—people matter, and companies must be prepared to change culture. The workforce must accept lean, not have it pushed upon them.

Preface

Things that are considered world class are universally admired as being the best at the present time. The Tampa Bay Buccaneers in the U.S., like Manchester United in the UK, are world class. Tiger Woods and Michael Schumacher are also currently world class.

World class manufacturing is synonymous with being "lean." The Toyota Production System is widely acknowledged as being the leading example of lean manufacturing, where the emphasis is to minimize or eliminate any activities that do not add value. As a result of this, work in a Toyota plant flows through consecutive processes rapidly, smoothly, and with minimal delay. This is totally different than the production processes that can be found in most factories, where a similar observation will see work dawdling and stuttering through separate operations in large, cumbersome batches. With all the delays that large batches cause, the finished product eventually leaves the factory as part of a shipment after a protracted period that stretches into several weeks.

A great many factories over the years have been taking selective elements of techniques such as SMED, TPM, Poke-Yoke, TQM, JIT, and 5-S Housekeeping, and applying them in their own manufacturing operation to suit their own requirements. During the past several decades, new breeds of managers, supervisors, and production engineers have developed who are well read on these subjects and are eager to progress beyond the traditional manufacturing methods still practiced by their employers. But, despite entering the 21st century, these piecemeal efforts have not resulted in large-batch production beliefs and functionally laid out processes being superseded by better techniques. An important reason for this is that there has not been a unifying set of rules about what key changes should be made and which of the new methodologies need to be implemented first, second, and third.

Lean manufacturing has emerged as the most complete and profound philosophy of how to maximize the potential of a manufacturing organization. Lean is that unifying rulebook of how to be world class. Instead of replacing JIT, SMED, 5-S Housekeeping, TQM, and TPM, or claiming to make them obsolete, lean actually incorporates many of their individual parts and connects them seamlessly into quite simply the best way to manufacture products.

It is a myth to think that lean manufacturing is the normal way that Japanese companies organize themselves, just as it is a myth to think that lean is unnatural to Western culture. Those Japanese companies, like Toyota, that have become lean have struggled to get there, encountering similar resistance and unwillingness as would be found in Western factories. The only way many Japanese companies actually got to be lean was out of a desperation to survive in circumstances where they faced intense competition and a shrinking market demand for their products. Even stubborn employee resistance can be overcome when the alternative to dramatic change is massive redundancies or even closure. In truth, lean isn't a natural way for anybody to think or any company to operate, irrespective of geography or culture.

Large companies can afford to spend considerable budgets educating and training their employees in lean manufacturing. They can employ external consultants or develop internal lean facilitators to drive change through the organization. But in smaller companies, there are fewer resources available to make the fundamental changes necessary to become lean. Small to medium sized enterprises (SMEs) will struggle to prevent improvement changes decaying back to the traditional practices they had before. This is because the majority of their employees won't buy into new ideas while their deep-rooted understandings and beliefs about how to best manufacture products remain unchallenged.

In many ways, changing an organization to the extent that it becomes thoroughly and permanently lean seems an enormous task. There are untold numbers of reasons why there will be resistance to such efforts, and innumerable points at which the change process seems doomed to failure. So, can an established SME on a brown-field site ever become lean, especially if it smugly believes that it is moderately successful remaining as it currently is? No, significant organzational change is required to suceed, and three fundamental building blocks must be in place before a lean revolution can proceed favorably.

1. *Knowledge.* The key people who have the authority to change the way things happen need to have a thorough understanding of their own company, why traditional practices are so undesirable, and how to think and act lean.

2. *Commitment.* The key people who can authorize and implement change must have the will and determination to go ahead and really do

it. Can they be motivated? Do they have the commitment? Do they feel empowered enough to take the necessary actions without seeking universal consent at every step? Are they prepared to do things differently, and are they prepared to make a few mistakes along the way?

3. *A Catalyst.* There needs to be a spark, a bang—something that is going to change the direction in which (until now) the business has been going. There needs to be a "change-leader" who will get everyone's attention and start to steer a new course. He/she will need a tight-knit core team of "lean disciples," who will form a plan of action, how it's going to be done, who's going to do it, and when.

Knowledge about lean is growing. There are many books and magazine articles available, written by academics or consultants, to explain specific manufacturing techniques such as JIT, TQM, Kaizen, etc. However, many of the available books are lacking in truly practical advice on how to make change happen successfully and permanently. The inevitable conclusion for the executive team in a business is that it will be necessary to employ specialist consultants to make the required organizational transformation happen. Using consultants often results in only a brief injection of training via workshops and shop floor blitzes, which do indeed result in some immediate and profound changes. But the change process will need to continue long after the consultants have left. If the company doesn't develop its own team of lean disciples, then the change process will stutter to a halt, leaving the business a long way from becoming truly lean.

In spite of the lack of practical implementation advice, these books and articles are still read voraciously, enabling us to stay informed about the latest "new thing" and the most recent business success story. When change agents read these books, they get flashes of inspiration, seeing how they can implement some of the techniques within areas of their own companies. Unfortunately, the occasional individual making a few changes in isolation from the rest of his/her co-workers cannot prevent the perpetuation of traditional practices. Singular improvement changes often prove short-lived and, in most cases, a lone person interested in implementing lean will be unable to make any real progress.

If you own your own company, or are at the level of being a director, it is different. You already have the power and influence to start a lean revolution. So start changing now, don't wait for the company to find itself close to bankruptcy before the organization realizes it has to do something significantly different.

But if you are a middle manager, how can you get involved in implementing lean? First, don't be a sheep. Speak up and get involved. Stand up for lean and support it whenever the opportunity arises. If the company hires lean consultants, get in on the action. Become a lean disciple. Request to be part of a "Lean Team" if one is formed. If you change jobs, move to a company that is implementing lean changes and get involved. Sell yourself on your knowledge and understanding of lean and on your commitment to improvement. Then demonstrate that you support change.

This book is first and foremost written for doers and change agents. It touches on all of the key points required to become a lean practitioner. Examples are provided where necessary, and there are lots of implementation tips and frequent words of caution. All the topics discussed have been successfully implemented and used.

There are fantastic opportunities to vastly reduce the waste in our factories, to help our manufacturing companies do more of what they should be doing—making a healthy profit at the expense of competitors. If you are fortunate enough to be deeply involved in this drive for improvement, the sense of achievement and job satisfaction for you and your team will be immense. Stop dreaming of being lean, and make it a reality.

Chapter 1

Removal of Waste

The Activity That Makes a Factory Lean

Most of us would agree that reducing waste in a factory is a good thing, but you would probably argue that getting operators to work faster and tackling quality problems are issues that require more immediate attention. When you begin to understand lean, you will realize that waste reduction is the *only* thing that should be in the forefront of one's mind, the *only* thing that should be driving us to change things for the better. Waste removal is lean. As a byproduct of becoming lean, productivity will naturally increase and rejects will be inevitably reduced. If waste is so important, how can we define it?

> *Waste is any activity that consumes resources*
> *but delivers no value to the customer.*

The Seven Wastes

1. *Defects in Products.* Having spent time making a unit only to find that it is faulty, then having to spend additional time repairing the fault, is a very obvious waste of time and effort. It would be better for the unit to be assembled properly the first time around. Components within faulty units occasionally have to be scrapped, wasting the money invested in purchasing those materials and any assembly labor associated with them.

2. *Overproduction.* Building products that are not immediately required is waste. Adding extra units to the real quantity needed, "just-in-case," or simply building to predefined batch sizes in an attempt to be more efficient, is also wasteful. The materials used in these overbuilds does indeed eventually get sold as product, but operator and machine time is wasted building something that is not immediately required, instead of everyone being focused on the most urgent work priorities at hand.

3. *Work in Progress (WIP) Queues.* This is where components have to wait their turn to be processed because of the characteristics of large batch production. Queues are synonymous with inventory: the larger the inventories—i.e., work in progress (WIP)—the greater the queuing. A half-finished product waiting in a queue of WIP is time being wasted. Queues lengthen the overall production lead time and their presence reduces the manufacturing system's flexibility. WIP is also a wasted investment of the company's money—it is money that has been tied up in materials that are not being allowed to quickly turn over to generate positive cash flow and profit.

4. *Unnecessary Processing.* It is wasteful to overdesign products. Specifying a material finish that isn't essential, or using more components than are really needed, or designing in features that the customer won't use and doesn't need, are all wasteful. Trying to identify and eliminate rejects through inspection is also unnecessary processing.

5. *Unnecessary Motion/Movement.* Operators can waste a lot of time performing activities that don't add value and could be avoided. Reaching out a long way across one's workbench for parts, then having to put them the right way up because they were stored in a disorganized manner, then double-handling the work or the hand-tools (having to pick things up and put them down several times) is all very wasteful.

6. *Excessive Transport of Parts.* Arranging processes "functionally" and spacing them far enough apart to allow sufficient space to accommodate all the WIP causes the total distance that materials travel to be unnecessarily great. Transporting parts takes additional time and incurs additional cost. If operators move the parts themselves, they are being taken away from value-adding work. If indirect workers do it, the overhead burden increases. If conveyor belts do it, floor space is wasted. A conveyor is a nonvalue-adding piece of machinery, a waste of capital investment, and an obstruction to the work area that then takes time to walk around. Though palletizing the WIP reduces the frequency of transport movements, it may also require widening the gangways (wasting more floor space), and the lead time will increase due to the greater WIP quantities in the system.

7. *Waiting People.* When people wait for a machine process to finish before the next part can be loaded, when they have to wait for a storeman to bring them the parts they need, or when an operator stops while an inspector checks his work, time and money are being wasted.

In summary:

Defects in products	= wasted time and perhaps also material
Overproduction	= wasted time
WIP queues (Inventories)	= wasted time
Unnecessary processing	= wasted time
Unnecessary motion/movement	= wasted time
Excessive transport of parts	= wasted time
Waiting people	= wasted time.

It is interesting to note that all of the above, except for any scrapped material, is fundamentally *wasted time*: sometimes machine time (capacity), sometimes operator time, and often component time (excessively long lead times). It is so true to say that "time is money."

Gaining Experience in Recognizing Waste

Lean manufacturing is the result of having removed such wastes. Because most of this waste is not in fact "material," it can be hard for some people to visualize time as a highly significant form of waste with enormous repercussions for the business's competitiveness. Becoming an expert in classifying what activities are wasteful is the beginning of the journey toward becoming a lean disciple.

Recognizing wasteful activities can sometimes be very simple; for instance, when an employee suggests that the company buy a conveyor belt to move material from one side of the factory to the other in order to remove the need to transport it all manually by using pallets and pump-trucks. While this would indeed seem more "efficient," transport activity would be better reduced by bringing the processes closer together.

Another "easy" example would be a situation where it is suspected that print operators are failing to catch all of the rejects coming from a screen printing operation, as several rejects from their area are reaching the downstream assembly process. The printer's excuse is that they don't have time to inspect properly—at the output rates that are required, it just can't be done. The Quality Manager hears of this and asks one of his roving inspectors to do an audit on their work every half-hour. What will this achieve? The direct operators concerned can indeed spend more time printing product, but they will now lose the ownership of quality, and the number of rejects is likely to increase. The root cause of the problem has not been identified, and the business has instead added an extra process that wouldn't be necessary if a short period of indirect effort focused on permanently removing the cause of the rejects.

In another scenario, a new employee questions why a particular "flash test" is carried out on all electrical products when there never appear to be any failures resulting from it. In his mind, he thinks it is a waste of time. Actually, such a test is being performed so that the factory's products can be assigned UL or BEAB approval. Manufacturers are responsible for ensuring their products are safe, therefore any test that is carried out for a safety reason is not wasteful. It may be the case that the consumers have been educated to buy only certain products if they have an Underwriters Laboratory or British Kite Mark. Electricians will pay extra to know that the electrical product they will be fitting inside someone's home is UL or BEAB approved and fit for purpose; therefore, the flash testing is adding value.

Defining whether a certain task or situation is wasteful can be quite difficult. Long-held intuitive beliefs cloud our minds. To avoid being confused about whether activities are wasteful or not, there is a simple questioning technique to apply:

If I did more of this activity,
would the customer pay me any more money?

With this in mind, consider the following three scenarios.

Situation 1

Let's employ an indirect person to take the bothersome "wasteful" jobs away from the direct workers, e.g., to refill the component bins, clean away the factory rubbish, and generally move parts from one department to the next. Surely this will allow direct labor to spend more time building product.

Response

If there were just one or two indirect people employed to perform these tasks, then the suggestion might appear to make some sense. But what if far more workers than this were employed, e.g., 20? Would the customer be happy to accept a higher price because of the greatly increased labor cost for the company's products? Of course not.

These indirect activities are waste, no matter who does them. Instead, the component supplier could deliver parts to exactly where the customer wants, not just drop them off with the goods-in storeman. Consecutive operations can be brought closer together; then less effort is involved in transporting work from person to person. Much can be done to minimize the amount of nonvalue-added labor that is required. Components could be supplied preorientated in blow-molded trays; packaging could be designed to be reusable and to stack so that buildups of discarded packaging, and the need for making trips to the skip, could be reduced. The need to clear away rubbish, or the effort in replenishing component bins, is only limited to the extent of the imagination of your team's suggestions. When activities such as removing rubbish have to be carried out, there is always "spare" operator time available at points throughout the shift to perform it.

Situation 2

The reject rate level seems to be on the increase, and this waste needs to be brought back under control. Experience tells us that more inspection will reduce rejects, resulting in the reduction of waste. In this instance, faulty subassemblies are only being discovered at the end of the production line when the product is fully assembled. Management suggests that each operator should inspect the work of the previous operator, so that no further work is done to a subassembly that is already faulty. This will avoid a fully built assembly being rejected, as the reject will be identified as a subassembly—at which stage it will be easier to rework.

Response

At face value, the suggestion seems to make sense. However, what if each operator checked the work from the upstream person 20 times before performing his operation on the workpiece? Would a customer be willing to assume such additional costs? No. Inspecting out waste and rejects is the costly way of solving quality problems. Nonconformance is due to excessive variation that takes a component's features outside of the acceptable limits. The presence of rejects means that there is insufficient control in the process. No human inspection process would ever reliably find 100% of all the possible faults anyway. It is better to identify and correct the reasons for the excessive variation and bring the process under control. Statistical process control can then be used to measure levels of process variation, so that processing adjustments can be made before rejects begin to appear. Additional inspection costs cannot be passed on to the customer, who expects quality to be built in as standard.

Situation 3

Our press setters are very experienced and work very hard to perform changeovers as quickly as possible. If they say it can't be done quicker, it can't—they're the experts. And since all the WIP we build does eventually get sold, nobody can argue against their opinion. It would therefore be a waste of time to set up the press for only the 300 or so components that are needed each day. Once the job is up and running, we might as well run off the whole coil of strip which lasts us a good three months, then we can forget about it and get on with something else.

Response

The customer would not be willing to pay for setters to spend more of their time performing changeovers, but they would have no objections if the company performed three times the number of changeovers if they were one-third of their present duration. If this were possible, it would be a very useful improvement, the benefits of which would be smaller batches and more process flexibility. Setup time is wasted time that *could* be spent producing product. However, it is always possible to find ways to reduce setup times if there is a willingness to make the effort. Making assumptions about things is dangerous. Do the setters really understand SMED (single minute exchange of die) techniques? Have they really challenged the way they are approaching their changeovers? Is their housekeeping really world class?

Alternatively, the company might purchase material stock supplied in smaller coil lengths. Perhaps the material could be supplied not as coil stock, but as lengths of flat strip? Could second-hand presses be cheaply acquired and left permanently arranged for those jobs that have lengthy setup procedures? The bolsters on the current presses could be redesigned (e.g., standardized) so that jobs can be changed far more easily and quickly than before. Or, perhaps consider outsourcing the stampings altogether, if it is not really part of the company's core business.

Traditionally, Which Form of Waste is Most Significant?

Rejects or scrap may be the most obvious problem, but to think that they represent the biggest proportion of all the waste in a factory is incorrect. They should be considered symptoms of problems elsewhere; they are the result of a badly designed manufacturing system. To attack the symptoms by increasing inspection would be ineffective and short-term, like trying to stop a common cold by sealing up the nose. Instead, it is important to pinpoint the causes for the rejects and scrap, and to correct them. The process needs to be changed to make it easy to manufacture correct product every time, and to make it extremely difficult to produce rejects.

Before any other possibilities are suggested, people naturally think of waste first and foremost as rejects. This is because rejects are tangible and easily quantified. It is typical for senior managers and accountants to expect to see regular and detailed statistical reports about the levels of rejects and scrap levels. In order to satisfy the demand for this data, the supervisors on the shop floor will closely monitor and record such information. Unfortunately, it is all too common that the result is not a concerted effort to reduce rejects—it becomes just another accounting exercise. Ask yourself when an accountant last asked for data concerning lead times or average setup times.

The way in which most shop floors operate makes it very difficult to discover and understand the real cause behind a reject occurrence. With so much WIP in the production system, the time that elapses between producing a reject and detecting it downstream is usually very great indeed. The supervisors are so distracted by expediting work through the system, making WIP counts to help their decision making, and dealing with more urgent issues, that little time is available to concentrate on the possible causes of rejects. Such quality problems have always appeared in the process, and everyone assumes that they always will. People become resigned to the "fact" that rejects are a part of everyday production. Trying to reduce scrap and rejects, while getting product out the door in an old-style production environment, is very much like the old proverbial saying: "it's difficult trying to drain the swamp when you're up to your backside in alligators."

The Types of Waste Most Significant to Lean

The two biggest evils are, in fact, overproduction and queuing time. By focusing on reducing these two, dramatic improvements will occur. To continue the analogy, these two wastes are the causes of the swamp being there in the first place, and if the swamp is taken away there will be nowhere for the alligators to live.

Another analogy that is commonly used is to compare a traditional factory producing large batches to a wide and deep river. Large rivers flow slowly and their depth easily conceals any boulders and obstructions in the riverbed. A traditional factory with large amounts of WIP is like a large river in which the boulders are the causes of rejects and the obstructions are reasons for machinery breakdowns. The speed of the water flow represents how fast work can move through the factory (i.e., lead time). As the water level is lowered, the river begins to flow faster and at the same time the largest boulders start to break the surface and become visible. To keep the river navigable, these boulders must be removed, allowing smoother and easier water flow.

This is what happens when you begin to make a factory lean. By reducing batch sizes, obstacles such as reject occurrences, material stockouts, and machinery breakdowns are soon encountered. Traditionalists would see this as evidence that lean is making matters worse, and that the water should be allowed to return to previous levels. But, in fact, this is an opportunity to locate and scrutinize these problems clearly for the first time so they can be understood, resolved, and permanently removed.

The Evils of Overproduction

Overproduction is usually deemed to be necessary by both supervision and production operators alike. It becomes accepted that rejects will always occur, and people choose to live with the fact and compensate for it when setting the quantities for the parts they decide to produce.

Overproduction is done "just in case." If the customer cell downstream receives too few units, there is a risk that the job will very quickly have to be set up again, having only just been changed over to start work on the next priority. However, will the customer cell complain if they receive a few extra units? Invariably, the answer will be "no."

In addition, everyone has a natural tendency to round numbers up to whatever number is seemingly appropriate at the time, usually up to the nearest convenient level (i.e., to the nearest 5, 10, 25, etc.). This also makes the mathematics easier. Appreciating this "just-in-case" habit of human nature makes it easy to understand how a requirement for just 32 units can grow to a production quantity of 40 units, or even more. In reality, not just one but several people will be tempted to bump up the numbers along the entire length of the process. Does it really matter, though, if it all is going to get used eventually?

The Consequences of Overproduction

1. *Fixing rejects becomes a very low priority.* With spare units constantly being supplied, any rejects can be replaced immediately and the shipment to the customer proceeds without delay. The pressure then will be to proceed with the next requirement straight away. The rejects that are removed from the system are cast aside into a "bone pile," and often some components from this reject bone pile might be cannibalized when the next material stock-out happens. Soon the bone pile grows dauntingly large. The temptation will be either to scrap-off a proportion of it, or palletize some of it and move it out of the area to prevent congestion. Without fixing rejects promptly, the root causes for their failures are not identified. Making more rejects of the same failure mode

becomes an inevitability. Even if the rejects *are* at some point repaired, perhaps in a quiet order intake period, the time that has elapsed since they were produced covers up the investigative trail. Properly fixing the causes of the problems is therefore next to impossible.

2. *Loss of production control.* If overproduction is widespread, who is making the decisions on just how big batch sizes should be? Just about anyone on the shop floor—from setter to operator—that's who. Their decisions will be made based on intuitive beliefs that big batches are more efficient. This will lead to ever-increasing quantities of WIP, thereby tying up cash and killing any hope of short lead times.

3. *Increased mix-ups, mistakes, and confusion.* The overbuild on fast moving, frequently used lines may not pose too much of an issue for traditionalists. However, surplus units of slow moving, occasionally required product lines end up sitting around in the production area for many weeks or even months. There is a high risk that they may be picked up by mistake and accidentally shipped to a customer. Spare units of "stranger" product lines are also at risk of going out of date or becoming obsolete. As product revisions occur, any old stock that remains must either be reworked or scrapped.

4. *Valuable time and resources are wasted on building product that is not a priority.* Working on priority orders is very important, but every time we overbuild by a few units on the current job, the longer the delay will be before the next priority gets started. Will overtime be needed to finish the next job because the build schedule has been delayed? Will the delay result in time running out before the day's last order is produced, even though there would have been time for it originally? Will the customer get the full order quantity a day late, or will a more expensive overnight carrier be used? Do you send a partial shipment, and then have to repeat some of the administration activity to send the balance at a later date?

Overproduction causes the factory to consume valuable raw materials on units that are not required, increasing the risk that components may run out on the next job. Additional materials end up being purchased to feed the wasteful increase of WIP.

The Evils of Material Queues

The traditional organization believes that it is optimum for every operation to work as fast as it can when it is in action, resulting in the formation of WIP buildups wherever imbalances in the maximum work rates between two consecutive operations occur. This means WIP buildups form between most operations. If only some of the faster operations were allowed to run at a pace similar to some of the slower ones, this WIP could be avoided.

It is also traditionally believed that, first and foremost, everyone on the shop floor must be kept busy. This principle is deemed far more important than the idea that everyone should be working on the right job priorities. This mental block also encourages the generation of WIP that is not immediately required. This results in yet another problem—should more money be thrown after bad? Either the unnecessary WIP materials wait around until there is a real need for them, or further processing is done to finish them into completed products so they can leave the shop floor and be packed away in the finished goods (FG) store.

What Causes Material to Queue

1. *A slow process feeds one that is much faster.* It would be a waste to have the downstream operator waiting for each unit of work to come along, so he/she gets on with some fill-in job elsewhere. This allows a buildup of work to accumulate, and after a period of time the downstream operator can come back and process the WIP that has accumulated. This happens on a larger scale when a multishift operation feeds a day shift area.

2. *A faster operation feeds a slower one.* The upstream operator will not want to keep stopping just because his downstream workmate cannot keep up. He/she will continue to work at the pace of his/her own job, and only move off to another operation when a reasonable buildup has been created, or until there is no more space to store the work. This happens on a larger scale when a day shift area feeds a multishift operation.

3. *A machine breaks down and stops processing work.* If the upstream operations continue to run in order to keep operators busy, a queue of work builds up.

The Consequences of Material Queues

1. *Large amounts of WIP form in boxes, trays, bins, pallets, and on conveyor belts.* WIP does not come for free; it is an expensive lodger. You have to double-handle it (put it down only to pick it up later and reorientate it for the next process). It must be stored, undamaged but readily accessible. If WIP builds up to the level where it needs palletizing, then you are likely to need bigger aisles and bigger doors, extra trolleys, pallets, pump trucks, sack trucks, fork lifts, and even additional

employees to handle it. What proportion of your factory is taken up by value-adding machinery and value-adding assembly benches, and how much is taken up by materials, aisles, and gangways? In a lean factory, it might be 70:30; in a traditional factory, it could be between 50:50 and 40:60.

2. *Inflated cost of overheads.* Floor space is expensive, but complacency over its use is easy. The rental charges on the building may be set for the year, so the costs are fixed. It is not possible to rent only the 89% of the shop floor that one requires. It is not possible to get a discount for leaving part of the floor space clear following a reduction in WIP. With such logic, the fatal trap is sprung: people start to think, "so why not utilize all the area available to us by spacing equipment farther apart?" Or, "what is so wrong with using up some unused space to store some 'just-in-case' materials?"

   However, as a company experiences growth, and new product lines are added to the existing range, there is a requirement for additional production space. The risk is that while WIP is taking up an unnecessarily large amount of floor space, there may be a decision to rent additional space or move to a bigger facility. The cost of moving the site or of running a split-site operation is considerable, so avoiding such a situation is important. The WIP that is taking up 40% of your floor space is also being kept warm, well lit, sheltered, and dry. This costs money. The gas bills, electricity bills, and other indirect costs attached to looking after WIP gets added to the total overhead cost proportioned to each product, and this has seriously adverse consequences. Reducing overhead improves profit margins. Products with minimal margins can be made more profitable when work is carried out in a lean manner.

   Wherever WIP exists in an operation, it costs money to manage. Resources are used to inventory it daily, weekly, or monthly in order to assess the state of production. Even then, additional WIP counts will be needed anytime an urgent order needs to be expedited, or when an important delivery date is required. The supervisory time wasted in counting WIP is time that could be better spent improving the process by reducing setups, eliminating the causes of rejects, developing individuals, and building better teams.

3. *Increased lead time.* The greater the quantities of WIP, the longer it takes for a single production unit to get completely through the system. WIP is simply work queuing to get through the process. It takes a long time to go on every ride in an amusement park when it is full of people

and there are large queues. The time taken to experience all the rides would be minimized if there were no queues at all. Quoted and demonstrated lead time is an important measure of customer service.

4. *Reduced responsiveness to changes in demand.* When there are long queues, there is a reduction in the responsiveness of the process to react to changes in demand. This is due to several reasons. The machines are unlikely (as of yet) to be organized for quick changeovers. The operators are used to processing work in a first-in, first-out manner, so it takes an expeditor to rush the urgently required product through the entire system. The poor proximity of parts and the large total distance the product will have to travel simply takes longer to organize than in a lean system.

5. *Poor culture of ownership and teamwork.* The very fact that WIP takes up lots of space means that sequential operations (benches/machines) have to be spaced farther apart. This makes it hard for neighboring processes to communicate with each other, and makes it more impractical for operators to move around from one job to another. A side effect of operations spaced apart is to create a poor culture of teamwork. It encourages isolation and makes sections territorial and partisan. This culture then breeds a feeling of lack of ownership and responsibility for the quality of the products being made, and encourages different parts of the production line to have priorities dissimilar to one another.

6. *Reject investigation and corrective action are hampered.* When there are large WIP queues, the elapsed time between a reject being produced to the time it gets discovered makes it very difficult to determine how or why it was caused. Therefore, no "permanent fix" can be determined. A lack of ownership for quality arises, because whether or not the finished product is correct has little significance to anyone but the very last people in the process.

Summarizing Lean Waste

The two greatest wastes that are equally important to attack when thinking lean are overproduction and material queues. Eliminating overproduction reduces WIP, and in doing so makes the system more responsive. Complacency about rejects is reduced and valuable resources are not wasted on product that has no immediate sales value. Large material queues are the result of blindly trying to maximize the efficiency of every individual part of an operation, despite the inevitable consequences of massively long lead times and the need to space neighboring operations still farther apart.

The traditional production ideologies that cause and justify these wastes are having crippling effects on manufacturing businesses. Until the paradigm is broken in each factory by a determined team of committed lean disciples, traditional beliefs will continue to be falsely legitimized.

Next, it is important to understand why WIP is loved so much by so many, and how setup times—the one legitimate reason for having long production runs—can be cut to a fraction of their traditional duration so that batch sizes can be dramatically reduced.

Chapter 2

Work in Progress

There are many reasons why WIP is encouraged and why people accept the consequences of it being around. To understand this is an important part of lean learning.

Why Operators Like WIP

1. *The feel-good factor.* A worker surrounded by piles of WIP looks to any passing observer like they are fully occupied. Operators will often leave a half-filled or nearly-full tray of work at the end of the day so that in the morning it doesn't take long to send the first tray down the conveyor belt to the next downstream operation. The operator feels like he/she has a head start in the morning.

2. *Musical chairs.* When nearly all the WIP containers are full, it becomes important for operators to be first to get their hands on the last few empty ones. At this point, people can literally come to blows. Without a couple of empty trays beside them, they won't be able to continue working for long and they may get put onto an unfamiliar job, in an unfamiliar area, with unfamiliar people.

3. *Fortress me.* The "old-style" operator, who perhaps is used to the work coming to him/her at "his/her" bench, rather than having to move to where the work is, will feel comfortable being surrounded by WIP, and very uncomfortable with no WIP by his/her bench. Piles of WIP are something to hide behind, which makes observation by supervision difficult. It allows, for example, coats, bags, sandwiches, and newspapers to be secreted. A busy operator feels secure: he/she is needed and won't be moved to another job that might be harder than the current one—a job that he/she might not be so good at.

Why Supervisors Like WIP

1. *Just in case.* An operation making subassemblies will often keep some

finished parts in their department as well as the quantity stored in the proper location by the customer cell downstream. This is for "just in case" reasons, and it also allows the supplier cell to run bigger batches than they might otherwise be allowed to do. When the downstream process panics because they think they've run out of a subassembly, the hidden cache of parts can be uncovered and the leading hand becomes a hero for the day. Fire fighting has this tendency. Leading hands and supervisors have been conditioned to believe that the praise they get when they have doused yet another fire is a reward well worth receiving. Therefore, fire fighting (mending a broken machine/tool or expediting parts) is an activity worth performing. In truth, fire fighters are not what the organization needs. What the company needs is corrective actions being put in place, process improvements that will help to develop lean production, and good housekeeping. It needs machines that receive preventive maintenance so they no longer break down.

2. *Keeping people busy*. When there is a lull in order demand, or a critical piece of machinery breaks down, operators will be given "fill-in" jobs. This usually means building up subassembly WIP or preparing parts for what the supervisor is sure will be required later—i.e., components needed for the big-selling product lines. This will feel like a safe thing to do, and a strategy that nobody "upstairs" could argue with.

3. *Maximizing output*. Because most traditionalists believe in maximizing the efficiency of every operation, the old-style supervisor will try to keep the best specialists for each job on those jobs for as long as possible. One side effect of this is that very little cross training occurs and employees can find themselves stuck on the same job for years.

4. *Looking after number 1*. When a supervisor has specific production targets to hit, it is always safer for him/her to try to keep any spare people even though they might be needed in another department that is struggling due to a shortage of operators. It is selfish, but supervisors will often try to retain unneeded workers in order to guarantee that their own production quantities are achieved ahead of schedule. Getting ahead of schedule, however, means building products that are not yet required: this is WIP building.

5. *The operators can look after themselves for a while*. From time to time, a supervisor will be preoccupied with something other than making sure only the right products are being made in the right quantities. In such situations (a coffee break, for instance), operators will tend to just keep

building what they are currently building until they run out of one of the components. This happens because the only rules for building up work are the rules that the supervisor makes up on the spot.

6. *Reduced supervisory effort.* Sometimes a supervisor won't know what jobs are required, because the call-off sheet hasn't been received yet or the mainframe computer that generates it has crashed again. In such a situation, the supervisor will continue to have some of the operators build the runners and other operators building up subassemblies of WIP. In order that a supervisor doesn't end up running around too much asking operators to stop that, start this, stop this and start that, he/she will find it easier to allow WIP buildups to occur. Bigger batches mean less intervention and that means less supervisory effort.

Chapter 3

The Importance of Bottlenecks

A bottleneck is the rate/capacity limiting factor in a production system. Know where the bottleneck is and you will know the system's maximum production capacity. Also, by controlling the bottleneck you can control the output level of the whole system, assuming that the supply of materials from upstream is not limited. When you learn to recognize the bottleneck operations in your own factory, you will observe that some of the largest WIP queues will be found just upstream of them.

Occasionally, the bottleneck process is not even within the limits of the shop floor. Where there is a glut of process capacity, the bottleneck is the lack of sales. This can be because of adverse market conditions, ineffective/insufficient sales marketing activity, or simply an uncompetitive product. The bottleneck might equally be the lack of availability of a single component due to worldwide supply limitations. However, for the purposes of this discussion, we shall consider it to be the rate limiting operation within the production system.

Bottlenecks are unlikely to be labor-intensive assembly jobs because it is relatively easy to add some extra assembly benches and hire a few extra people. The production bottleneck is very likely to be a single piece of machinery, such as a press, a heat treatment oven, an expensive test bench, etc.—items that are difficult and/or expensive to duplicate. The cycle time of that piece of machinery then becomes the capacity constraint of the whole process.

It is highly feasible that a bottleneck machine for one product type is not necessarily the bottleneck machine for a different product type, so it pays to know your process! Know your bottlenecks to the point of knowing that when the product mix being manufactured is altered, you can predict where the new bottleneck operation will be.

Having bottlenecks is a fact of life. Eliminating one bottleneck by buying a second heat treatment oven to cope with the increase in required output, for example, merely makes the next slowest machine the bottleneck. It is similar to building a bypass around a town: it probably allows fractionally more traffic to flow, but the worst traffic snarl up point simply moves from the eased junction to a point somewhere just down the road.

When justifying the capital to buy the second heat treatment oven, it should be anticipated that the systems throughput is unlikely to double; it will increase only to the limitation of the new bottleneck operation. If the purchase can still be justified, then go ahead with it.

Assessing if the Bottleneck's Capacity Can be Increased

The most obvious thing to investigate with a bottleneck is why throughput rate is limited to its current level. The process you need to go through to try to get a bit more output through a bottleneck is like the techniques you will need to use when trying to reduce machinery setup times. For example, can any unnecessary "human" actions be done within the machine's cycle time instead of outside of it, so that the overall bottleneck cycle time is reduced? In the time between cycles, where parts are unloaded and loaded, is everything immediately at hand and in a convenient orientation? Does the operator use both hands effectively when unloading and loading it? E.g., does the left hand unload the processed part, *at the same time* the right hand loads in the next part? Does the machine's jig/fixture make it difficult to load and unload? Does it have 1) chamfered guides, 2) rounded location pins, and 3) quick clamping devices? And, finally, if during the processing time the operator is performing other value-adding work, does it prevent him/her from being ready for the end of the bottleneck machine's cycle? If not, the time lost from the bottleneck by such a delay is lost forever.

Does the leading hand, and all the operators in the area, know the importance of their bottleneck machine? Are the operators taking split breaks so that the bottleneck is always being operated throughout the day? Are you sure they aren't going to concentrate on some other issue, such as trying to maximize the labor efficiency of the team? This would be a noble undertaking indeed, but if downstream operations are being starved because the bottleneck in the upstream area is being under-manned and therefore underutilized, then it is a misguided one.

Because the bottleneck is likely to be a piece of machinery, it is probably going to have to be set up each time a batch of work of one type is changed over to the next job priority. Of all the machines to attempt to dramatically reduce the setup times on, this is *the* machine that common sense dictates you must make SMED a priority improvement action.

Using Knowledge About a Bottleneck to Optimally Plan Operations

Overtime

You will be able to calculate levels of overtime required so that your production system's bottleneck is running for enough hours to satisfy current demand. This might mean (unfortunately) building up WIP in front of the machine in normal hours to allow an overtime worker to keep working on the bottleneck machine throughout the evening.

Preventive Maintenance

Complacency over a bottleneck machine breaking down is rare. It receives immediate fire fighting attention. However, Murphy's Law dictates that it will break down when you most need it to be running. In preference to this, a preventive maintenance schedule should be drawn up to avoid breakdowns occurring. In this way, a small amount of servicing time can be performed for a known number of minutes at a specified moment of *your* choosing each week, instead of the machine breaking down at a random time and for an indefinite duration.

Planning Upstream Operations

Prevent starving the bottleneck of work by planning the upstream operations very carefully and ensuring that they in turn are not starved of components, or are themselves disrupted by breakdowns.

Reject Cause Elimination Effort

Reduce the rejects that the bottleneck might inadvertently end up processing (which would be nonproductive processing and therefore wasted capacity), by ensuring that all work that is fed to it has zero defects. Focusing attention on reject elimination efforts here, rather than elsewhere, will pay the greatest dividends. Not only is rework effort avoided, but the amount of overtime required on the bottleneck machine will be reduced. Unfortunately, allowing rejects to be processed through a bottleneck is all too commonplace, thanks to the complacency that most people have about matters of quality: believing that rejects within a process are an inevitable byproduct of manufacturing.

Conclusion on Bottlenecks

By ignoring bottlenecks, or by paying little attention to them, a significant amount of lost production capacity will certainly occur over time. Time lost at a bottleneck operation can't be regained except through costly overtime (*if* this can be arranged, and *if* the operation isn't already working 24 hours a day, 7 days a week). A lean disciple should not only strive to become expert in identifying waste, he/she should also strive to become an expert on their factory's bottlenecks.

Chapter 4

Setup Time Reduction

Becoming lean revolves around removing waste from the operation. The two biggest wastes are overproduction and WIP queues. There is one "real" issue that must be overcome in order to greatly reduce batch sizes without increasing costs. This is the need to reduce machinery setup times. Some very specialized books have been written on setup time reduction, and there are numerous training courses on the subject available to help your company in this area. *This* book does not intend to go into microscopic detail about all the many ways in which changeover times can reduced, because it is not all that complicated. Making it happen in your operation is simpler than many experts would have you believe. After all, it pays the consultants to be vague about the SMED process (<u>s</u>ingle <u>m</u>inute <u>e</u>xchange of <u>d</u>ie) until you have signed up for one of their on-site workshops. However, because setup time reduction is crucial to facilitate lean manufacturing, the recommended process for achieving it will be presented here in a few pages. Even though this information may be brief, you will find it very useful.

1. *Gather a suitable team together.* There should be a setter, an operator, a production engineer, an engineering manager, and perhaps the person responsible for maintenance. It is best to have at least six participants.

2. *Briefly train the team.* Explain the difference between "internal setting" (setting tasks that can only be carried out while the machine is stopped) and "external setting" (preparatory tasks that can be done before the machine is required to stop, or tasks that can be done once the machine is up and running again).

3. *Video an entire setup.* Pick a fairly typical setup job and video record it from start to finish. Make sure everything—right from the very first thing that has to be done—is caught on film.

4. *Review the video in detail.* Back in the training room, review the process on a TV so that everyone can observe it clearly. Ask everyone to note all the

different tasks being carried out during the entire setup (some people will spot activities that others will miss). "Post-it" style notes are good for this because they can be moved around on the table, sorted, and split into the two categories of internal and external tasks as will be required later. Also, arrange for one person to record the time elapsed each and every time the setter begins a new task. This will provide the duration of each task, as can be seen in the following example.

Time	Task Duration	Task Description
10:30	—	Stop Machine
10:32	2 min.	Find and get ready new processing material
10:36	4 min.	Fetch the tools and equipment that are needed
10:37	1 min.	Put on personal protective equipment
10:48	11 min.	Clean and prepare the new tooling
10:52	4 min.	Remove machine guards
10:54	2 min.	Remove the old tooling
10:56	2 min.	Fit the new tooling
10:58	2 min.	Fetch the new material and feed into tool
11:10	12 min.	Adjust the new tool as required
11:12	2 min.	Perform first-off quality audit
11:16	4 min.	Replace machine guards
11:18	2 min.	Clean and maintain old tool
11:20	2 min.	Put tools and equipment away
11:23	3 min.	Dispose of remnants of old material
11:23	—	Start Machine
53 minutes		**Current Changeover Time**

Encourage the team to observe how far the setter has to walk during the setup, how long he/she searches for the correct tool due to poor housekeeping, and how awkward it is to remove and replace the tool from the machine. Why is the time spent on making all the operational adjustments so great? Why are all the adjustments necessary? Can't the required settings be known and prepared for, beforehand?

By this point, everyone will begin to clearly see the opportunities for setup reduction. Now, split the ~6 people into three roughly equal groups, A, B, and C.

5. **Team A:** *Improve housekeeping.* One team always gets the "boring" jobs, doesn't it? But there is plenty involved in this.

   A. Reorganize the materials so they are easily accessed, clearly identified, properly orientated—ready for lifting and moving, and organized so they won't be damaged by careless stacking or unnecessary handling.

   B. Define the gangways (using tape, or paint, to make clear lines on the floor) to allow permanent access to materials, emergency exits, machinery, etc.

   C. Arrange tooling so that they are easily accessible, clearly identified, orientated ready for lifting and moving, and organized so they won't be damaged by careless storage.

   D. Organize equipment better, have a tooling preparation/setup bench on wheels so it can be brought close to the machine when needed to reduce "unnecessary movement." Is there a *full* set of Allen keys or sockets available? (Or can we organize that only one or two sizes are ever needed and they are permanently attached to the wrench handle?) Is it obvious where to store the different pieces of equipment so the setter always knows which drawer to open for what piece of tooling?

   E. Set in place a housekeeping audit that can be performed quickly.

6. **Team B:** *Separate the internal tasks from the external tasks.* Separate the individual setup activities according to whether they can be performed only when the machine is stopped, or whether they can be done while the machine is still running (or has started up once again).

Internal Tasks	External Tasks
4 min. Remove machine guards	2 min. Find and prepare new processing material
2 min. Remove the old tooling	
2 min. Fit the new tooling	4 min. Fetch the tools and equipment needed
12 min. Adjust tool as required	1 min. Put on personal protective equipment
4 min. Replace machine guards	11 min. Clean and prepare the new tooling
24 minutes Internal Setting	2 min. Fetch new material
	2 min. Perform housekeeping audit
	2 min. Clean and maintain old tools
	2 min. Put tools and equipment away
	3 min. Dispose of remnants of old material
	29 minutes External Setting

Without really "improving" anything, we can straight away reduce (by more than half) the setup time from 53 minutes to 24 minutes.

7. **Team C:** *Reduce the task times (especially internal).* What can be done to reduce the number of tasks to be carried out while the machine is stopped? Good housekeeping will go a long way to reducing the duration of the external tasks. Would two people performing the setup help to reduce the internal setup duration? Can the fixtures for securing the tooling be modified to facilitate mistake-proof location and a quick clamp/quick release? Do all the bolts being used need to be turned so many times; can the thread length be reduced? There are several catalogs available from tooling component companies that specialize in quick connectors, quick release clamps, etc. Use their products; it doesn't all have to be invented by you and your team.

Can electric/pneumatic drivers be used to speed up the task of removing and replacing bolts? Can the removable safety guards be secured with fewer bolts (i.e., one or three sides of the guard locate themselves in a lipped frame permanently fixed to the machine, and when the remaining side is bolted down all sides are now held firm)? Improving the housekeeping in this area (and especially the manner in which the setter's tools are stored), and ensuring that the setters have the best tools to do the job, will shave not seconds but several minutes off many of the individual task times.

Optimized Internal Tasks		Optimized External Tasks	
1 min.	Remove machine guards	1.5 min.	Find and prepare new processing material
1 min.	Remove tooling		
1 min.	Fit new tooling	1.25 min.	Fetch tools and equipment needed
5 min.	Adjust tool as required		
1 min.	Replace machine guards	0.25 min.	Find and put on protective equipment
9 minutes Internal Setting			
		9 min.	Clean and prepare new tool
		2 min.	Clean and maintain old tool
		1 min.	Put tools and equipment away
		2 min.	Dispose of remnants of old material
		17 minutes External Setting	

Now we have reduced the changeover time from 53 minutes to just 9 minutes! We have achieved Single Minute Exchange of Die, SMED.

When all the changes are implemented, practice setups as if they were Grand Prix pit stops. This will help to emphasize the importance of setup skills as it applies to performing changeovers in the shortest possible time. Have a notice board in the area where the "internal" and "external" setup tasks are written down.

Once the SMED workshop has accomplished its goals, it would be a good idea to congratulate the team by having before and after information to show the improvements that have been attained. To keep the housekeeping up to standard, a housekeeping audit will be necessary to keep the area organized. Finally, to keep the gains made and monitor further progress, record and chart the setup times being achieved. This follows the fundamental truth that if you want people to know something is important, or needs improving, then it is good practice to measure it and have a chart showing the results displayed in the team's area, preferably produced by the leader of the section (see **Figure 4.1**).

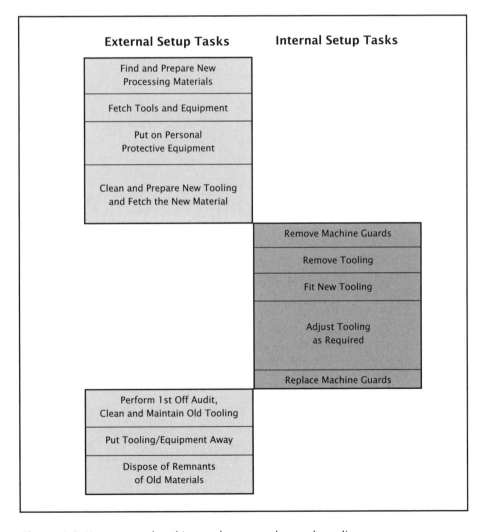

Figure 4.1. How external and internal setup tasks can be split.

Chapter 5

Batch Size Considerations

Big batch sizes are usually the result of trying to maximize "up-time" efficiency on large machines that have lengthy setup times—such as injection molders, extrusion lines, and stamping presses. Downstream of these machines, in areas that are more likely to be labor intensive, big batches are encouraged because operators and old-style production supervisors think that lots of WIP is useful and convenient stuff to have around. However, traditionalists are blissfully unaware of the following harmful effects on the business.

1. Work queues prevent quick and effective response to increasingly demanding customers.
2. Inventory value present on the shop floor can be so great that it literally strangles cash flow to death.
3. Reject causes are obscured, and rejects become accepted as a production byproduct.
4. Large batches cause overhandling of the work by operators, resulting in lost productivity.
5. Usable space is wasted, causing increased overheads and reduced profit margins.
6. Payroll is burdened by employing storemen, production planners, and expeditors.

Assuming a factory does have some method for determining its batch sizes, what are the "traditional" considerations borne in mind? First, it will be highly likely that the planner will plan different length runs for different processes in the factory. The reason for this is that different families of machines will typically have different setup durations. A traditionalist would expect a machine to run for perhaps twenty times as long (or more) as setup time, but, pre SMED, that represents a very long run duration.

Material containers are a secondary factor. What number of units could be conveniently stored in the most appropriate type of container (e.g., 34 units to a tray)? It would be more convenient to make the batch a direct multiple of that quantity (i.e., 12 trays of 34 units) to avoid partially filled containers (especially when there aren't many containers to spare because so many are tied up holding WIP). The container issue will vary in different areas of the factory. As the product gradually gets assembled (getting bulkier and changing shape) and moves downstream, the containers that are convenient to use at each stage will change. For example, thousands of stamped clips supplied from the press shop can be held in a single bin, but maybe only seven fully assembled products can be stored in a standard tray. The planner's obsession with filling the container may make bins of metal components weigh far too much, making them impossible to carry without a trolley. A spinoff benefit of lean manufacturing is that the vast reduction in WIP allows heavier components to be stored in bins in greatly reduced quantities, preventing the risk of any manual handling strains.

Lastly, batch size might be decided by a philosophy of making sufficient components "in one go" to represent, for example, 1–2 weeks or even a month's worth of requirement by the customer cells. The planner thinks in these terms because the size of a batch has a lot to do with the rate of consumption for that part. In fact, it can be more practical for a planner to think of batch sizes as "time buffer" quantities rather than as mere physical quantities.

Batch Definitions

"A batch" is the term normally used for the quantity of a particular product to be made all in one go. An entire batch of work might take several days to complete. Traditionally, this would involve the "batch" going through one operation at a time, and it wouldn't be allowed to go to the next operation until the entire batch quantity had gone through the current stage of processing. The batch is kept together like this to allow the roving inspector a chance to compare the components from the beginning, middle, and end of the batch to specification, all at the same time. The batch can only continue to the next operation when the inspector signs it off for quality conformance. It also allows the batch to be kept together so that WIP counting is easier.

In a lean process, the term "batch" becomes almost meaningless. Big batches are now split and overlapped. The work required to be completed that day is allowed to be processed through several different stages concurrently. Overlapping and breaking down of the build quantity allows small transfer batches to be pushed through the system. The transfer batch size is the number of units that an operator consecutively puts through one operation before he/she stops and moves to a different workstation. The lean operator does this because to stay on the same job for any longer would just keep building up WIP in an ineffective manner. The only operation that is allowed to run for the majority of the time is the slowest one (it might be run continuously if it is the bottleneck operation).

The Effects of Reducing Batch Size

The simplified theoretical model shown in **Figure 5.1** illustrates the effect of batch size. Just three different batch sizes of 12, 5, and 1 units are shown being processed through a simple five-operation production process. "Op Two" is the slowest job of the five, with a process time of 4 minutes, and is being continuously utilized. The different shades are there simply to show the separate transfer batches—they do not signify different products.

It is clear that, in a situation where no expediting is taking place, smaller batch sizes greatly improve response lead time of the process, and this is achieved without reducing the total throughput capacity of the system.

The vertical dashed lines shown on the model are the points at which two WIP counts were made, so that an average operational inventory level can be estimated. **Table 5.1** shows the performance data. Assigning fictitious costs to each stage of the product's assembly state helps to demonstrate the material cost each scenario carries.

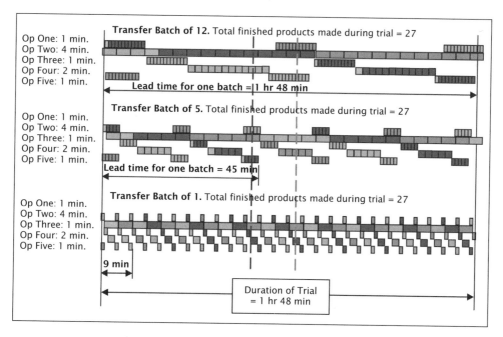

Figure 5.1. The flow of transfer batches through a simple system.

		Operation Unit Cost	First Line WIP Count	Second Line WIP Count	Average Material Cost on Shop Floor
Batch size 12	Op one	$1	4	8	
	Op two	$2	8	11	
	Op three	$3	2		$76.50
	Op four	$4	10	3	
	Op five	$5		9	
Batch size 5	Op one	$1	4	2	
	Op two	$2	4	3	
	Op three	$3			$32.50
	Op four	$4	2	3	
	Op five	$5	3	2	
Batch size 1	Op one	$1			
	Op two	$2	1	1	
	Op three	$3	1		$5.50
	Op four	$4		1	
	Op five	$5			

Table 5.1. Example of performance data used to estimate average operational inventory.

This example, though oversimplified, strongly suggests that the relationship between batch size and WIP cost is directly proportional, as is the relationship between batch size and lead time (see **Figure 5.2**). Therefore, one can consider inventory to be effectively the same as lead time. The simplistic conclusion is that if you halve your batch sizes, both your inventory and your lead time will halve.

Let's explore how a team of workers might take different approaches to completing a day's build requirement to illustrate the range of alternative ways it can be achieved. The same cell used in the previous example will now be given some more realistic work to process. The cell still has the same five operations in which to completely build and test its family of products. For today, the cell is asked to produce 100 "A" products and 60 "B" products, which should require the three people in the cell approximately 8 hours (the full day) to build.

1. The worst approach to tackling this workload (given sufficient duplication of equipment) would be for all 160 units to be processed through the 1st operation by the three people. Then the team pushes all of them through the 2nd operation, etc., as shown in **Figure 5.3**.

This results in very poor workflow, with the A and B products only

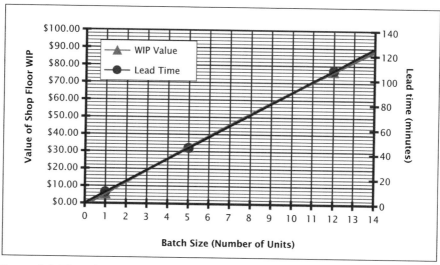

Figure 5.2. The relationship between batch size, WIP, and lead time.

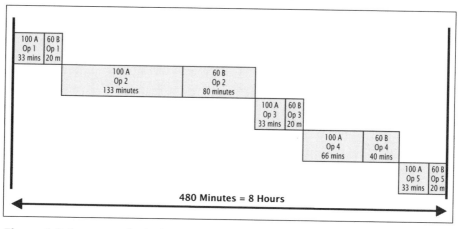

Figure 5.3. A poor method of work flow.

being finished at the very end of the day. Any rejects are only discovered after 7 hours go by.

2. The next worst plan of action, as shown in **Figure 5.4**, would be to build all the A product first, then the B's, but still with all three operators working on the same operation at any time.

   Using this approach, it will take 4 hours and 25 minutes for the first A to appear out of the system, and the B's will not be completed until the very end of the day. There is still a high risk that the entire batch of 100 A and/or 60 B products may be found to be faulty.

3. A far better scenario would be for two of the operators to share the work from operations 1, 2, and 3, and the third operator is dedicated to operations 4 and 5, as shown in **Figure 5.5**.

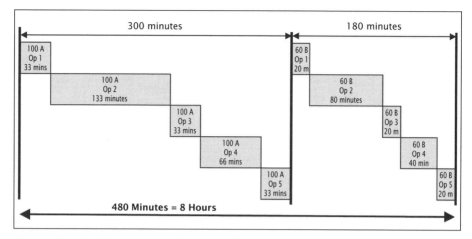

Figure 5.4. A slightly improved method of work flow.

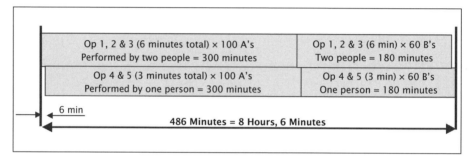

Figure 5.5. A greatly improved method of work flow.

Now, at least, there is a better flow of work. Finished A products stream out of the cell at a rate of one every 3 minutes for the first 5 hours. Then, for 3 hours, finished B's emerge one at a time. Any reject is found very quickly and the customer is no longer in a feast-or-famine situation. The way in which all the A's come out first, followed by the B's, is totally appropriate for many, but not all, situations.

What if the completed B's were not finished products, but merely finished subassemblies that are required in yet another cell, and that this downstream customer cell has a testing machine (only used for B subassemblies) that is the overall bottleneck of the process. Under these circumstances, it wouldn't be acceptable to starve the downstream cell with the bottleneck operation of B's for most of the day. To avoid losing process time in the bottleneck, the downstream cell would have to have a WIP pile of waiting B's to keep it going through the first 5 hours of each day.

In situations such as this, there is a third alternative where the production grouping of A's and B's is broken down still further. How much the production quantity is subdivided depends on the needs of the customer cells downstream and the flexibility limitations of the supplier cell. Here are four possible work-splitting variations:

AAAAAAAAAAAAAAA**BBBBBBBBB**AAAAAAAAAAAAAAAA**BBBBBB BBB**, etc.

AAAAAAAAAA**BBBBBB**AAAAAAAAAAA**BBBBBB**AAAAAAAAAA**BBB BBB**, etc.

AAAAA**BBB**AAAAA**BBB**AAAAA**BBB**AAAAA**BBB**AAAAA**BBB**AAAAA **BBB**, etc.

AA**B**AA**B**AA**B**AA**BB**AA**B**AA**B**AA**B**AA**BB**AA**B**AA**B**AA**B**AA**BB**AA**B**AA**B** AA**B**, etc.

Being able to split the work like this is the ultimate in flexibility: the production cell can now supply the customer operation downstream in any style that is required.

Minimizing Transfer Batch Sizes in Labor-Intensive Cells

When there is a product that can be assembled and tested without the constraint of setup activities, then the size of the transfer batch can be reduced to the absolute minimum of one unit. Depending on the quantity of components and the work involved, there are two methods of making what is commonly known as *one-piece flow* a reality.

The first situation is where the product is small and simple (i.e., without too many individual components), and it can be fully built and tested by one person at one bench (see **Figure 5.6**). The objective is that the operator can build one and test it before building the next one and testing it, etc. Any rejects are found immediately and the repair work is also carried out immediately. The operator soon becomes expert in the product's manufacture, its characteristics, and its flaws. He/she then immediately starts to learn what factors are causing the rejects to crop up. What needs to be done to avoid these rejects quickly becomes apparent, and the employee begins to offer lots of suggestions for improving the build design and mistake proofing the build process so that reject levels are greatly reduced.

The second type of one-piece-flow application is in a multiple operator assembly cell, as shown in **Figure 5.7**. This is appropriate when the work can be split into small divisible amounts, so that a small number of people can be organized to work together at the same speed by sharing the work equally among themselves. However, workload adjustments may be necessary each time the line changes from one product in the range to a

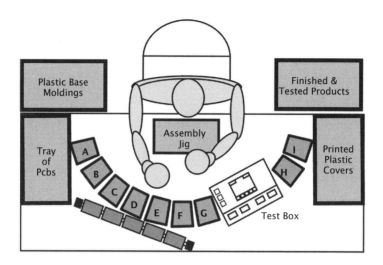

Figure 5.6. One-piece flow with a single operator on a single bench.

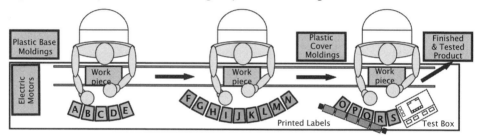

Figure 5.7. One-piece flow for three operators using three benches.

subtly different one that might have a slightly different component mix, or just a different number of the same components.

The team needs to understand the following lean rules so that one-piece flow becomes a reality.

1. Balance the workload among each operator, so that everyone's unit-build time is as close to being identical as possible.

2. No queues of work are allowed between operators. Only the three pieces of work that are having value added to them are allowed on the line at any one time.

Minimizing Transfer Batch Sizes in Machinery-Intensive Cells

One-piece flow is also possible in some machinery-intensive operations such as the one shown in **Figure 5.8**. Even though it may not be possible to totally overcome the setup complications to gain better process flexibility, the machinery can still be utilized during a production run in a style of one-piece flow. This will allow the business to enjoy gains from having far less WIP, and of having a greatly reduced number of rejects.

By ignoring the misguided belief that all machines should be operated at maximum throughput rate, it becomes acceptable to see machines stopped for short periods as long as they are not the slowest operation. We now understand that the total throughput rate of the system is always limited to the slowest operation, and this is true of the machining cell in **Figure 5.8**. Operating the other machines any faster than the slowest machine will not alter the quantity produced each day, it will only increase WIP inventory. The machining cell can be operated with one or two operators who load and unload single parts through each stage of the machining and finishing process. They are trained to work according to the rules of one-piece flow. In this case, the machines cannot be unloaded just so they can be reloaded, unless the next downstream operation is vacant. The only exception to this is when the cell has to be put on overtime to meet the level of customer demand. Under these circumstances, because the slowest machine has now become a bottleneck, you now want an unloaded part waiting for the bottleneck operation to finish its current cycle to enable a quicker workpiece changeover. This will help to maximize the bottlenecks uptime.

Optimizing Transfer Batch Sizes When One-Piece Flow is not Possible

Every cell is different, and you will find there is no "hard-and-fast" formula

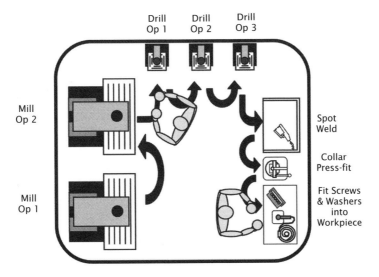

Figure 5.8. One-piece flow in a machinery-intensive two person cell.

to determine the optimum transfer batch size. A degree of experimentation is needed, where different limits to the work buildups (transfer batch size) are tried; e.g., 4, 5, 8, 10 units, etc. You may find that eight units works well in one cell, and sometimes this number will be safe to use in other very similar product cells. A different transfer batch size may need to be set for a section that has different working techniques, tools, or numbers of parts to be assembled.

A compromise will have to be made between keeping the number small, which will promote a faster flow of work through the cell, but not making it so small that the operators are becoming less productive because they are moving around too much relative to the time they spend adding value.

Experimenting with different ways of working might arouse suspicion and concern for most shop floor workers who tend to assume that the end result is always to make them work harder. Therefore, it is best to select a few individuals who are sufficiently multiskilled to be able to work flexibly in any of the cell's operations, and are enthusiastic, open-minded, and prepared to try something new. Everyone you pick needs to be a willing participant who is going to be fair and unbiased during the trials.

Begin by briefing the three to four operators you have selected so they feel involved and know what to expect, and will be more able to provide constructive feedback afterwards. You should explain the following.

(a) They should work at a constant rate that they could maintain all day.

(b) When they are asked to build a set maximum number of units, it applies to all workstations and they agree to stick to the set quantity for the duration of the trial.

(c) The intention is to run four trials (for example) with different transfer batch sizes, with each trial lasting the same length of time (e.g., 1 hour).

(d) The cell is to be "primed" in the same way before each trial begins: for example, half-quantities of the transfer batch size will be placed between each consecutive operation to allow the cell to work from the beginning without a "cold" start.

(e) In the event that the agreed transfer batch quantity has been reached, or the workstation runs out of work, they are to move to another workstation where work is waiting to be processed. This is likely to be quite a new concept. For it to work, everyone will have to work as a team and help each other keep the work flowing. No one is to wait for work to come to them; work has to be chased through the cell.

(f) The amount of work completed over the duration of each trial is going to be counted because productivity is undeniably important. Furthermore, the length of time it takes a unit to go through the cell from start to finish (without expediting it) is going to be timed and recorded, because improving the speed of workflow is a goal of the trial.

Before the first trial is performed, allow a short warm-up period so the operators can get used to chasing the work around. Then, reset the WIP in the cell to the "start-up" levels. After each of the four trials, quantify the results, make observations, and ask for feedback from the team.

When the trials are complete, an informed decision can be made about what WIP buildup can be allowed between successive operations in the cell. If, for example, the quantity is eight units, that quantity can be fixed as the number that is to be used by everyone who comes to work in this cell. Enforcing this quantity can be achieved by doing several things.

1. Pick a work container (a tray or rack) that can hold just eight units. If required, modify it so it is impossible for it to hold more than this number. You may need to put dividers in the tray, permanently block off some of the tray holding locations, or cut the rack down to the desired size.

2. Limit the number of trays available to the operators. Don't have any "spares" on hand that can be used.

3. The containers modified to hold the desired number of units must be made conspicuous enough so that no similar looking containers can be brought into the cell without it being immediately obvious that cheating is going on.

4. Anyone working in the cell needs to know, understand, and keep to the new rules in place for this lean cell. They are: chase the work; never exceed eight units between successive operations; and work together as a flexible team.

5. As soon as it is noticed that any of the rules have been broken, the cell must be put straight and coached to work as agreed. Cell meetings are an excellent forum for exchanging ideas and making adjustments. However, beware of suggestions that the team should revert back to large batches. Be firm and rebuff such challenges, but do not give the impression that you are not prepared to listen to constructive ideas for improvement.

As other cells that work along the same lines are implemented, the culture of the shop floor changes and the limitations on WIP buildup are accepted as the norm. Any operators who feel that they can't work as part of a team should be assigned jobs where they can work on their own. Good coaching can help most people adapt to lean working, but it is not worth compromising the effectiveness of an otherwise good cell, or making a stubborn individual unhappy, to force people to fit into a situation that is alien to their personality.

Post SMED Run Lengths in a Machine-Intensive Area

Once all the SMED activities and actions have been made, most setups can be reduced to anywhere between 5 and 30 minutes, depending on the circumstances encountered. Setups in this region are still significant, so the guideline to follow is:

The production run should be five times the duration of the setup.

If you were to ask a machine shop or a press shop if they would be happy with 83% uptime, then many would reply "certainly!" As an example:

12 minute setup = 60 minutes of production run required before the next changeover.

Unfortunately, this may mean that if the machine cycle time is very short, you still may end up with several weeks or even months of components being produced during the run. Such a situation is unlikely to be a major issue because any component that is so fast to produce is likely to be very small and therefore of very little cost. This category of component also won't take up much space even at moderately large volumes.

Larger components are by definition bulky, and they will take up proportionally more storage space. Therefore, large quantities of these types of parts would use a disproportionately greater number of storage boxes than the smaller moldings. They will also tie up a large amount of inventory cost. Where you find larger components, you will probably also find that their machine cycle times will be much longer. A large power press with a big and heavy tool necessitates a slower strokes-per-minute rate. A large injection-molding tool would more likely be comprised of a single cavity and have a long cycle to achieve the correct mold result. A machining center processing a large part is likely to be removing a considerable amount of metal and will therefore take more time to machine each part. But, by adhering to the same rule—a ratio of 1 to 5—these more expensive components will be produced in far fewer numbers per production run, and the WIP held will be less. The 5:1 rule dictates that the jobs set up most frequent will be the larger components being machined or molded.

Additional Hints and Tips

Don't Ignore the Obvious

If there are spare machines (perhaps deemed spare because they are older or less flexible), *do not throw them out*. They could be left permanently set up for some of the jobs that are particularly awkward to set. Dedicated in this way, such a machine could be left idle for much of the time and only switched on to run those "odd-ball" components, as and when required. Perhaps an old machine could be used for a "runner" and kept on that job all day, thus allowing the latest machinery (designed for quick changeovers) to be used for the "strangers."

Beware of Misusing Newer Machinery

When a new CNC machining center or a new surface mount machine is bought, the Operations Director will typically expect to see that machine used all day long on big batch runs. This is because a high machine utilization rate helps to justify such an expensive piece of capital investment to the Financial Director. When new equipment is utilized in this way, it is commonplace that the older machines (often with a book value of zero), which used to perform the same work, are now hardly used at all. This is clearly madness. Such rules of accounting are taking the manufacturing system *away* from being lean and toward *uncompetitiveness*. Any production engineer who helps to specify and justify such new machines must explain in the request for capital expenditure that the machine will be used along lean principles. This will encourage the justification to be based on lean realities, and the outdated rules of running a business based on economies of scale won't be reinforced. Lean reasoning must be used to challenge and beat this institutionalized discrimination that wrongly favors big batches.

Use Continuous (One-Piece) Flow Wherever Possible

From what has been discussed so far, the advantages of one-piece flow should be clear. Use it wherever you can, but it will be impossible to achieve from the very start to the very end of the entire process. At the junctions between areas such as SMT (surface mount technology), the press shop, or an injection molding department (i.e., where batching is necessary) and a cell of continuous-flow assembly work, there will need to be a kanban to connect the two (as described in later chapters). The kanban will control what the upstream batch process produces, so that it only manufactures components that are being consumed and therefore need replenishing. This does away with the traditional (and flawed) need for a production planner to provide a work schedule for such batch processes.

The Problems of Planning Work in a Traditional Manufacturing Business

A production planner doesn't use tea leaves, and does not have some mystical sense of knowing the future. He uses the sales forecast for the coming month and the information he has about the current mix of WIP and FG stock to plan what needs to be produced over the coming 4–6 weeks. One thing we all know about the sales forecast is that it is inevitably inaccurate (often it is only 75% accurate). Also, it is common for the stock counts to have errors, especially when much of it might be stored many feet above head height on high-density racking. Therefore, one thing we know about every production plan and MPS (master production schedule) is that they will not be completely accurate.

But traditional planning has even bigger problems than this. Often the production planner, because of being tied to the materials department, has "tip-off" knowledge about what materials will be available and which won't be. He/she is not going to produce a plan asking the operators to produce things they won't be able to, so the planner regularly resorts to planning the build according to what materials *can* be supplied. This is a totally reasonable thing to do; it is not the fault of the planner. However, every time such allowances are made, it reinforces an acceptance of the flaws of the traditionally organized material supply system. But neither is the materials department to blame, as they are just working to whatever the goals and objectives the business school directors believe to be best. This is usually that the materials department should base most of its decisions on buying the lowest cost materials and minimizing both incoming and outgoing shipping costs. The materials department will only change its methods to help support lean manufacturing once the director to whom it reports fully understands and commits to lean manufacturing.

Frustrations for the Setters

Press shop, mold shop, and SMT production schedules as produced by the Production Planner will result in most batch-produced parts being either over- or underproduced. To minimize this haphazard situation requires the planner to keep making stock counts and keep issuing new, revised plans. Remember that this is all incurring indirect cost. Customers won't pay more for the goods so that a planner can issue twice as many revised plans—therefore it is a wasteful activity. The batch processors then end up performing setups for a job that is not really required, and then that job has to be taken down and replaced with the "screamer" jobs that are really important—the parts for which the downstream operations have just run out of.

Because the plans may have been written several days earlier, it is also common for jobs to have been planned for material that *should* have come in, but *has not*. In a non-SMED setup environment, the hard work of preparing the tooling changeover might get completed before the required material is fetched, and it is only then realized that the cupboard is bare and the setter's labor has been wasted.

Frustrations for the Operators

If your company is brave enough to do an employee survey, probably the two biggest complaints of the shop floor will be 1) anger at always running out of components, and 2) lack of information about what is going on. The combination of kanban boards and the use of faxbans (short-notice material call-off's faxed to suppliers on a regular basis), where leading hands are responsible for operating them, will go a long way to resolving the first issue. To some degree, these lean tools will also indirectly help to alleviate the second problem as well.

SMED in a Labor Intensive Area

Transfer batch sizes should be determined by how difficult it is to change over from one product to another. Never accept that such setups can't be shortened. Changeovers in work areas with little or no machinery are purely a matter of changing over component bins and assembly jigs and, as such, they can be very quick. To make this easier (and therefore, faster) color-code the component bins, e.g., yellow tubs for one product, brown tubs for the second, blue tubs for the third, and red tubs for the fourth. Then use a louvered panel on wheels that can be quickly brought in and out of the cell, this will help make the bin changeovers happen in as little time as possible. Any jigs and fixtures that are different for the different products need to be kept close at hand (good housekeeping) and should be colored for the different products in the same way as the component bins. If you have jigs that need to be screwed down to a bench top, have small pieces of removable "bench surface" that can be swapped quickly with either a blank piece of bench surface, or with another piece with a different jig attached.

Innovations like these will facilitate much quicker changeovers, and the barriers to shorter and shorter production runs will be removed one by one. But what do you do when even a small batch size exceeds the quantity required by the customer (or customer cell)? In this instance, a kanban will probably be the answer, so that moderately small quantities of product are held to buffer the cell from the variability of demand. Kanbans will be discussed in detail in later chapters.

Chapter 6

Analyzing the Leanness of a Process

Value-Added Time Versus Total Lead Time

Go into a factory and ask the supervisor what is the shortest time it would take for a "widget" product to go from the start of its manufacture to completion, and the reply will probably be "only a couple of hours if required." Supervisors will naturally think that the ability to expedite product through the system on occasions when this is required will be enough to keep everyone happy. In reality, it is common for the lead time to be several days, because of the time a product wastes sitting around in queues.

You may not consider the time a part spends waiting and queuing for its turn to be processed through each successive operation to be wasted time. Most of us think, quite rightly, that an operator waiting around is a financial waste, but somehow this doesn't apply to materials. The temptation in the past has been to keep everyone busy on various jobs around the factory. Because ultimately everything that operators have worked on will eventually get used, most people are reassured that such work is never *really* wasted. *Or is it?* These intuitive beliefs seem to have foundation, but in reality they are misguided and damaging to the health of the business. Yes, let everyone be busy, but let them be busy building things that are an immediate priority.

Every lean disciple must believe in the rule *thou shall not allow overproduction*. The waste caused by materials sitting around the shop floor is a crime against leanness, and the punishment is that your manufacturing system will be prevented from performing at anywhere near its true potential.

Comparing how much time a typical production unit spends having value-adding work done to it, to the total time it spends in the system before it pops out the end, well and truly finished, is ideal as a means of measuring the lean health of your process. A factory that has yet to start lean improvements can expect a depressingly unsatisfactory ratio of anywhere between 1:100

and 1:500. After carrying out some rudimentary efforts toward becoming leaner, a figure of 1:50 would be nothing to be ashamed of.

To help justify the changes needed to become leaner, an analysis of the value-added time a component receives, as a proportion of its total lead time, is very helpful. It is a quick study that is useful to do from time to time, especially before any changes are instigated, and should be repeated several weeks later once things have settled again.

As well as estimating the total lead time, it is worthwhile to log the number of hours of value-added time *and* the hours of testing time that are carried out. The best way to show this data is with a pie chart like the one shown in **Figure 6.1**.

Such a pie chart visually demonstrates where your production system is in terms of its "lean health." Some companies can be *a lot worse* than 99% of the lead time being nonvalue-added. Proportions as large as that are not worth discussing for any length of time—instead, they need acting upon.

Finding out the value-added and testing times will be easy. However, estimating the total lead time is more complicated, especially when it is likely to be very, very, large. There are two ways of performing this study.

1. Mark a component that is going to be made up into an initial

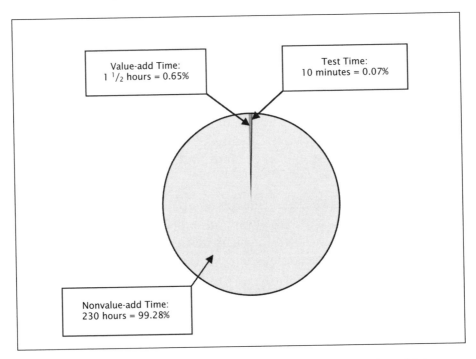

Figure 6.1. Nonlean example of value-add time compared to nonvalue-add time.

subassembly and thus one that will later go on to become part of the fully assembled product. Then wait for a finished unit, with that marked component attached, to appear at the end of the process. Sounds easy and straightforward, but do you want to wait a month to find out? Can you afford to have someone waiting at the end of the process for several weeks looking for the marked component, and are you prepared to take the risk that after all the wait it slips through the net and you have to start all over again? Can you mark a component that really does represent the start of the process and still see that mark without having to partially disassemble the finished product at the end of the line? Another risk is that the operators, who know there is a fuss over it, see the mark and then expedite it through the process. Can you trust the operators to treat the marked component like the rest? If you make the mark too discrete, you will make it harder to spot at the end of the process.

2. There is an easier way. By using the fundamental understanding of how batch work flows through a process, one can make an excellent estimate of the overall lead time. If you can determine both the sizes of each of the WIP piles waiting between each successive operation, and also the cycle times of each of those operations, then it is possible to calculate the total lead time of the entire process. For example, the time it takes for a batch of 100 components to get through an operation whose cycle time is 20 seconds is 2,000 seconds (33 $^1/_3$ minutes). Making this calculation for each stage of the process gives the cumulative lead time of the system.

Assuming FIFO/LILO, the wait for any component in the queue is the same, because our imaginary marked component has to travel from start to finish, it has to wait its full turn through each queue till it finishes the

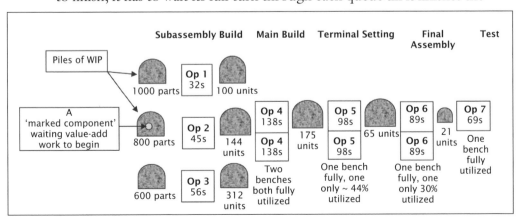

Figure 6.2. How the lead time of a process can be found.

last op. The only exception to this is the very first pile of components, i.e., the supplied material. Here, an average queue time should be taken. **Figure 6.2** is an example of such a value-added versus total lead time analysis.

A key rule that has already been demonstrated is that the throughput capacity for the cell is determined by the slowest operation. In this example, the slowest cycle is "Test," which is also the final activity performed. Therefore, it does not matter that some of the operations can work faster than this; the queuing time can be calculated as if every operation time was 69 seconds. Our imaginary marked component sits in the center of the pile of parts waiting to go through "Op 2." See **Figure 6.3** for a pie-chart analysis of this example.

Overall lead time   = [400 (half of raw parts) + 144 + 175 + 65 + 21] × 69 seconds

                           = 55,545 seconds

Value-added time   = 45 + 138 + 98 + 89 = 370 seconds (0.67%)

Note: this is the time that 'marked component' spends either on its own or attached to a larger assembly when it is having value-added work being carried out on it.

Test time   = 69 seconds (0.12%)

Nonvalue-added time   = 55,545 −370 − 69 = 55,106 seconds (99.21%).

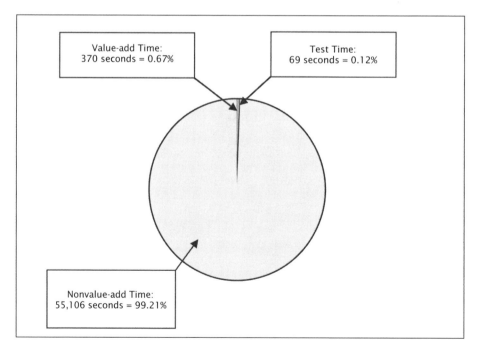

Figure 6.3. The value-add analysis breakdown of the practical example.

You will doubtless have your own opinions on whether overall lead time should be calculated to include the raw material waiting time as well as the waiting time of the product that is undergoing value-adding work.

One viewpoint is that lead time is all about a production system's ability to respond quickly to change, and that this is not affected by the magnitude of raw material stocks, simply on their availability and the assurance of speedy replenishment. Therefore, lead time should be measured from the first point that value adding begins to occur on a product (i.e., do not include raw material waiting time).

The other point of view is that all inventory in the system should be reduced to the minimum for true leanness. Therefore, to make sure that everyone's focus is on driving all forms of inventory down to improve leanness, raw component waiting times should be included in the overall lead time calculation.

Whatever your business decides is most appropriate, tailor the calculation to suit it and be consistent in the rules you have chosen to apply.

Chapter 7

Productivity and Lean

There are many arguments and counterarguments about whether lean production is more productive than traditional working methods. Arguments either way can be correct, but with a clear understanding of the issues any potential pitfalls can be avoided.

When a traditional-style production engineer tries to improve his/her manufacturing system, the effort will nearly always get directed toward making the value-adding time operations shorter (say, 5% faster, for example). Against an original production time of 1½ hours, an improvement of that magnitude would require about 5 minutes to be shaved off. This may save ~75 cents of labor cost from a product costing a total of $60 to produce, and this would help to bump the profit margin up 12½%, from $4 to $4.50. This sounds like a very successful achievement, but is it? Lead time, inventory levels, or quality levels are unchanged. So, on the scale of things, it has been a very lonely improvement result. The waste in the system and, to a great extent, the competitiveness of the business will remain unchanged.

Changes toward lean clearly focus on greatly reducing lead time by reducing inventory, but the changes to the workplace that are made can also affect productivity levels. Be highly skeptical about claims that lean manufacturing generates very large productivity increases; it can happen, but only in quite special circumstances. However, lean consultants will frequently state that lean can deliver *really big increases in productivity*. They do so because it is the main benefit that every Managing Director wants to hear. There are, in fact, just as many reasons for productivity being reduced rather than increased. Whether lean changes will result in productivity going up or down does not have to be left to chance—lean disciples can steer a "best course" if they know and understand the various "cause and effect" factors that are involved.

Reasons for Productivity Increasing Due to Lean

- Less time wasted double-handling materials.

- Less time wasted looking for tools and equipment (due to better housekeeping).

- Less time wasted walking around looking for parts, or waiting for materials to arrive.

- Less time wasted producing rejects, and then reworking them.

- Less time wasted in moving so many separate (unassembled) parts over such large distances.

- Some jobs might now be able to be done within machinery cycles because consecutive operations will now be much closer to one another.

All of these mean that there is more time available for building additional units. With operators taking ownership for their work and productivity, they will also be a far greater source of improvement suggestions for smarter, quicker ways of getting work done.

Reasons that Productivity Increases Will be Limited

- Perfectly balancing a "one-piece-flow" line, especially with 3+ people, is difficult.

- Multiskilling of cell workers means that much of the time they are not on their best/fastest job.

- Getting to a point where people are multiskilled requires a moderate investment in training time, which is done at the expense of output.

- Some individuals will inevitably try to take it easy and allow the team to carry them—they need to be identified and dealt with.

- There are more opportunities for line stoppages, especially until "new cell" problems are resolved and operator coaching imbeds the advantages of single/multipiece flow.

- Operators find themselves on many more jobs, becoming generalists rather than specialists. This may mean that, until mistake-proofing has been carried out, silly mistakes may happen more often .

- Each operator may be handling more tools and parts at each workstation because several jobs have been combined. This, and longer average reaching distances, may slow production.

One of the biggest individual reasons that productivity gains will be limited is the failure of the purchasing and sales departments to evolve toward leanness as well. The factory simply cannot be effective if it is forced to go through feast and famine situations, in terms of the materials being supplied to it. Neither can production be efficient if the orders the sales office requires result in large spikes and frequent barren periods. In a famine situation, the operation has to revert to the evils of part building, double-handling, and WIP creation to avoid having people stop working altogether.

Where Lean Can Attain Large Productivity Increases

It is true that lean production will be much more productive if it is implemented in an environment where the production equipment is spaced widely apart, and each machine has its own operator in place while it runs. Such operators are being grossly underutilized, only having to load and unload the machine. While the machine's cycle time completes, the operator stands around with little to do.

In the example shown in **Figure 7.1**, an injection molding area shows great potential for improvement as it currently runs with one operator resident at each press. The machines are far apart because of the quantity of WIP that is allowed to accumulate—WIP that obstructs operators from moving between the machines. Each machine has its own operator, just in case the feed runs out or a workpiece fails to eject properly. He/she is also required to inspect-out any rejects. Traditional job demarcation dictates that machine operators are higher graded workers, and that trimming, finishing, and packing are jobs for lower graded workers, and "this is the way it has always been done."

By setting down rules to limit WIP buildups, the machines can be moved closer together. It then becomes possible for one operator to run two or

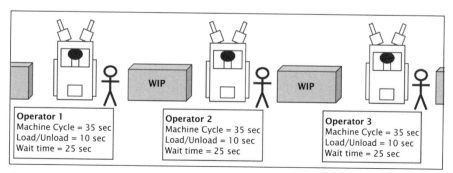

Figure 7.1. A situation where there is an opportunity for large productivity increases.

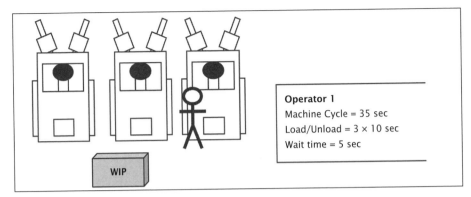

Figure 7.2. When machines are brought together, one operator can operate more than one machine.

more machines at once (**Figure 7.2**), moving from one to another as needed to unload the work, in order to keep the machines running. In this type of situation, lean has facilitated a localized productivity increase of 300%.

Where Lean Can Attain Small to Moderate Productivity Increases

When a traditional workplace with a series of unbalanced operations also has operators that are not flexibly moving around to help each other, a large amount of time gets wasted because most of the team is being kept waiting for the slowest operation. Though the operators in front of the slowest operation *can* go faster, they soon realize that a WIP buildup has formed and that they might as well slow down because their work isn't being consumed as fast as it is being produced. Operators downstream of the slowest job also end up working slower than they might, because they are being starved of work. This can occur on a microscale between bench operations, but can also occur on a macroscale between consecutive work cells.

In the following example, four people are tasked with sending out 100 refunds to customers. They are provided with a list of customer names, addresses, and refund amounts. The team has done this work before and decides to put the fastest operators on the slowest jobs to try and achieve a better work balance, and they divide the tasks between each other as described. So that mixups do not occur, they hand the checks and compliments slips along to each other one at a time and methodically work down the list from top to bottom.

Average Job Time		Job Description
Person A	25 sec.	Write check out and hand to Person B
Person B	35 sec.	Write brief note to addressee on a compliments slip
Person C	28 sec.	Write address on envelope
Person D	22 sec.	Take matching check and compliments slip, put in correct envelope, and apply 1st class stamp.

	Operator's "Natural" Speed c.f. Average	Work Study Time of Operation	Real Life Unit Busy Time (sec)	Unit Cycle Time (sec)	Person Wait Time/Unit (sec)	Individual Efficiency of Person
Person A	95%	25	26.3	32.4	6.1	81.2%
Person B	108%	35	32.4	32.4	0	100%
Person C	104%	28	26.9	32.4	5.5	83%
Person D	93%	22	23.7	32.4	8.7	73.1%
		110				

Task duration expected = (110 seconds × 100 refunds) ÷ 4 people = 2,750 seconds

Task duration achieved = 26.3 + (32.4 seconds × 100) + 26.9 + 23.7 = 3,316.9 seconds

It is clear that as long as the team works in this way, their overall efficiency will fall short of what is expected, being only 82.9% efficient overall, taking 55 min 17 s instead of the theoretical time of 45 min 50 s.

Alternative 1

The list is cut into four equal sections, so each person will reply to 25 different customers. The procedure everyone follows is to complete only one reply at a time. They also agree that anyone finishing early will help out any others still working by making a couple of extra replies for them. A new problem now emerges: there is additional handling of pens, check books, and envelopes since each must now be picked up and put down more frequently. This adds 5 seconds to the total value-add op time of 110 seconds.

	Operator's "Natural" Speed c.f. Average	Time of Operation	Real Life Unit Busy Time (sec)	Replies Done	Time Taken /sec	Individual Efficiency
Person A	95%	115	121.1	24	2906	100%
Person B	108%	115	106.5	27	2876	99%
Person C	104%	115	110.6	26	2876	99%
Person D	93%	115	123.7	23	2845	98%

Task duration expected = (110 seconds × 100 refunds) ÷ 4 people = 2,750 seconds

Task duration achieved = (slowest person) = 2,906 seconds

Because of the increased handling, the team has again fallen short of 100%. But this time they have worked more as a team and have achieved a 94.6% productivity score, taking 48 min 26 s instead of the original time of 55 min 17 s. So this is a greatly improved method for completing the job.

Alternative 2

The list is again cut into four sections, but this time, acknowledging the differences in their abilities, Person A agrees to reply to 24 customers, B to 27, C makes 26 replies and the slowest person D will do just 23. It is now allowable for each individual to write checks and compliments slips in multiples of no more than five at a time to reduce the amount of time being lost picking up and putting down equipment. They are told not to exceed this "transfer" batch size because beyond this it will unnecessarily risk a mix-up being made. The lost handling time of 5 seconds is now averaged to just 1 second per reply—one-fifth of what it was.

	Operator's "Natural" Speed c.f. Average	Time of Operation	Real Life Unit Busy Time (sec)	Replies Done	Time Taken (sec)	Individual Efficiency
Person A	95%	111	116.8	24	2803	100%
Person B	108%	111	102.8	27	2776	99%
Person C	104%	111	106.7	26	2774	99%
Person D	93%	111	119.4	23	2746	98%

Task duration expected = (110 seconds × 100 refunds) ÷ 4 people = 2,750 seconds

Task duration achieved = (slowest person) = 2,803 seconds

Now there is very little double handling of either materials *or* equipment. The team has worked very efficiently together and has achieved a 98.1% productivity score; their time is now 46 min 43 s, which is much closer to the "golden time" of 45 min 50 s.

This change has taken the production time for making 100 refunds from 55 min 17 s down to just 46 min 43 s, an improvement of 18%. The lesson to be learned is that because lean encourages a flexible workforce that chases the work rather than waiting for it, productivity can be greater than with traditional ways of working.

Where Lean Can Reduce Productivity

It is possible to blindly adopt one-piece flow to areas where it is not appropriate, believing it to be a panacea for all ills. A lean disciple can become so focused on reducing the double-handling of work that the bigger picture becomes clouded. One-piece flow will indeed produce the shortest lead time and the least WIP inventory possible, but productivity may in fact become suboptimized. In many circumstances, working on just one unit at a time greatly increases the time wasted in handling tools and equipment. These situations are likely to occur where there are many different hand tools the operator will need to use, and the duration that any one tool is needed is quite short.

Situation 1

Some small but expensive printed control boards ("pcbs") are held as part of a moderate volume of kanban stock, and these pcbs are customized at short notice to one of several varieties, depending on the demand from customer cells. (Kanbans, or "make-to-order" instructions, are scheduling systems that effectively limit the quantity of product being produced, thereby preventing overproduction.They are discussed in detail in later chapters.) This customization is done by adding a small conventional electronic component of the required value just prior to its assembly into a larger product.

The materials being used are a kanban tray containing the pcbs, some solder wire, and a tub of the components to be fitted. There are three tools. A "solder sucker" is required to clear two holes in the pcb of solder before the component can be inserted, a soldering iron is needed to fix the component in place, and a pair of hand snips will be necessary to trim the component's legs if they protrude too far from the back of the board.

The operator places six pcbs in a line on to the bench in front of her and, taking the solder sucker in her left hand and the soldering iron in her right, she removes the solder from all twelve holes one after another. Then six components are put into the waiting pcbs, after which they are flipped over onto their backs and from the underside they are soldered in place with the operator holding the solder wire in her left hand and the iron in her right as she goes. Having performed all the soldering in one go, the iron and wire are put down and each board is picked up and trimmed with the clippers where necessary, before being put down completed into a tray. To complete these six units has taken just 1 minute and 45 seconds. However, when asked to perform this minor task one at a time to a fresh set of six pcbs, it takes a longer time of 2 minutes and 20 seconds. This demonstration makes it evident that in this example it is 33% more productive to do 6 in a go than it is to do one at a time! Has lead time increased? Yes, but almost imperceptibly. Here the removal of waste that drives every lean action must conclude that the removal of time being wasted handling tools excessively is more important than blind devotion to one-piece flow of workpieces. A sensible balance can provide the best solution.

Situation 2

One particular type of product getting shipped to the customer has its own dedicated packing area and deals in delivery consignments of typically four shipments of 500 units each a week, making a total weekly packing requirement that averages 2000 units.

The first stage of this packing process is:

Op1	3 sec.	Take one unit from basket and place it on bench
Op2	6 sec.	Push in 2off permanent plugs into base of product
Op3	9 sec.	Push in 3off removable plugs into base of product
Op4	4 sec.	Stick wiring label to inside of terminal cover
Op5	12 sec.	Screw terminal cover onto unit
Op6	4 sec.	Stick free-issue label onto front of unit
Op7	5 sec.	Put unit into a polyethylene bag

Before any lean changes were made to the process, four packing benches were arranged end to end. Two packing operators worked together and put 30 units side by side along the run of benches, taking them two at a time from the baskets that are stacked several high on top of a wheeled dolly trolley. Then the pair works together to perform the operations to the 30 units one after another in succession. Each time the roll of labels, the tub of plugs, or the plug insertion tool has to be picked up and put down again it takes an additional 2 seconds.

	Time /Unit	Batch Size	Tool Handling Time	Total Time per 30
Op1	1.5	30	2	47
Op2	6	30	2	182
Op3	9	30	2	272
Op4	4	30	2	122
Op5	12	30	2	362
Op6	4	30	2	122
Op7	5	30	2	152

Thirty units in this prelean scenario take 1,259 seconds, or fractionally under 21 minutes, to complete.

In an effort to make the operation leaner, the two spare benches were removed and the remaining two were then separated and moved square to each other: ☐☐, rather than end-to-end. The packers were asked to work separately, packing just five units at a time.

	Time /Unit	Batch Size	Tool Handling Time	Total Time per 30
Op1	1.5	5	2	57
Op2	6	5	2	192
Op3	9	5	2	282
Op4	4	5	2	132
Op5	12	5	2	372
Op6	4	5	2	132
Op7	5	5	2	162

Thirty units now take 1,329 seconds, or 22 minutes 9 seconds. This may not seem like much, but it represents a 5.6% drop in productivity. In real life, the drop in productivity was even greater. The packing operators were more isolated with this new bench layout, and even greater losses in productivity were encountered because, in order for the operators to speak to each other, at least one of them would have to stop work completely. Far from reducing lost time, separating the benches like this had actually increased it; the real losses in productivity were closer to 10%.

Situation 3

A big implication for a loss in productivity with the implementation of lean techniques is on a macroscale. In traditional factories, operators can go on and on building product even though it is probably not for an immediate customer requirement. In the lean environment, the run lengths are shorter, there are far more changes in the product mix being built, and operators have to move from job to job very frequently. The supply of work from one cell to the next is much closer, being only a few trays instead of a pallet's worth. If supervision is not careful, members of the downstream cell may start to slow down because they know they aren't receiving enough material to keep them all fully occupied if they were all to try to stick to the normal/expected work rate. To prevent this, the leading hand/team leader needs to *monitor the productivity rates daily* from each of the cells and become expert in knowing how many operators each cell requires each day, for the rate of work that is required.

To help with this, the supervisor should have at his/her disposal a table of *how many operators in a given cell are needed to produce the various levels of output that will be encountered.*

Situation 4

Because of the increasing amounts of mobility required from the shop floor, there will be many cases where an operator is moved to an unfamiliar cell for a few hours or even a few weeks. The operator will have to learn some new components and be shown new, unfamiliar jobs. Some operators will see this as an opportunity to gain a wider knowledge of the company's products, which could stand them in good stead should a better job opportunity be advertised internally. Unfortunately, other operators will feel that such a temporary move is an opportunity to take it easy, they don't feel such a commitment to their temporary work colleagues as they do to their regular team, and so they work at whatever rate they like. Supervision needs another tool to prevent this causing a problem —*a comprehensive list of job times for their entire area.* A situation where an individual visibly slows down when it suits him or her cannot be ignored. The operator in question needs to be put on a job where he or she is not going to be required to move away from for a long period, and his or her work rate needs to be monitored against the standards expected.

If management is complacent about these individuals, then any positive work ethic that exists on the shop floor can easily spiral downwards because their workmates will quickly question why they too shouldn't take it easy. If this recommended course of action is taken with the worst culprits, then the majority of employees will see that individuals can't and won't get away with "free-wheeling," and the average work rate will be maintained at a good level.

Situation 5

It is quite possible to make mistakes when trying to change things for the better. One such costly mistake is to confuse the relative importance of (and different factors involved in) reducing WIP stock with the importance of reducing raw material stock (material waiting to begin the value adding process). For lean cells to be flexible, they need sufficient lineside stocks available to them at all times. It is easy to make indiscriminate and wholesale stock reductions in the misguided belief that it will aid lean. To get it right requires experience, planning, and careful calculations to decide on the optimum quantities of raw materials that each cell needs to "prime" it for action. Sometimes, cutting back lineside stocks even slightly can lead to highly disruptive stockouts that force cells into partial/incomplete building, having to build to wrong priorities, and having to increase WIP. The savings gained from taking a lineside stock of resistors down from 5 bags to 3 may save $30, but it can result in broken delivery promises, damaged customer relationships, and costly declines in productivity.

Reducing lineside stocks is desirable unless it costs you more than you gain. A typical reason for making overzealous reductions is incorrectly surmising that average rates of production (without high build rates) can be assumed when making calculations on maximum stock levels. Another mistake is to ignore the delay between ordering more stock and receiving it as a delivery on the shop floor.

Why a Sensible Application of Lean Will Increase Profits

1. With inventory (raw, WIP, and finished goods) being greatly reduced, there is less cash tied up in material holdings, and shop floor space is freed for additional production lines, reducing the overhead burden per product.

2. Lean production increases productivity rates thanks to less double-handling and fewer rework/repair efforts, resulting in improved profit margins.

3. Fewer production support activities are necessary. The number of storemen, planners, and expeditors will be greatly reduced, thereby lowering the overhead burden and again increasing profit margins.

4. The flow of work is smoother and more continuous. Month-end production surges that require a great deal of additional labor hours are eliminated, so the requirement for high levels of costly overtime is reduced.

5. In a traditional factory, the product lead time may be greater than the time customers are prepared to wait. In order to resolve this problem, companies will often ignore the fact that reducing material queues results in the reduction of lead time. Instead, the situation is used to justify the belief that it is necessary to spend capital on buying equipment

to achieve overcapacity at several places along the production route. In a lean factory, the work flows far more quickly through the process, and what might have appeared to be a bottleneck in a traditional process does not necessarily cause problems in a lean environment. Feast and famine situations are avoided, and the load on all operations is more evenly spread throughout the month. Fewer unnecessary capital expenditures mean less overhead burden, helping increase profit margins.

6. The most significant profit increase will come when the sales team seizes the opportunities of greatly shortened lead times to win more business with the customers. Because a lean organization can offer better levels of service, delivering "just-in-time," it allows the downstream customer to hold less stock than he ever thought possible, at considerable financial advantage to himself. The increased turnover this can generate for the lean manufacturer means increased revenues (at better margins for reasons explained above). A beautiful coincidence in becoming lean is that the factory will have been freeing up something like 25% to 40% of its shop floor space by massively reducing its inventory, and doing away with the old nonfunctional layouts where benches were spread so wastefully far apart.

Conclusions About Lean and Productivity

Traditionalists believe that large batch runs are more efficient. In some situations there is a partial foundation for this belief, if applied in moderation, but in most cases they are wrong. Correctly applied, lean is far superior.

➤ It is ineffective to improve productivity by a small amount and yet leave lead time unchanged. However, it is harmful to reduce lead times at the expense of being less productive.

➤ It is harmful to reduce lead times at the expense of being less productive, but ignorance about which changes have a real impact on productivity is not an excuse for failing to work toward becoming leaner.

➤ Moving from traditional incentive schemes that might include individual piecework, to one of team-based productivity measures, is a major cultural change for the better on the shop floor.

➤ It is easy to get carried away with the idea that every time an operator does some work it should be along the principles of one-piece flow. This isn't necessary or even realistic. The difference between one-piece flow and multipiece flow, in terms of lead time reduction, is at best minutes and at worst a couple of hours. Be happy that it is possible to get the overall lead time down to single-figure hours using multipiece flow in the majority of places, and don't become too obsessive with the ideals of one-piece flow.

➢ Monitor productivity levels before a change, as well as afterwards, and learn to judge the balance of how to reduce lead time at the same time as retaining satisfactory or improved levels of productivity.

➢ Monitor the productivity rates daily from each of the cells, so that the team knows how it has performed and can focus on what it needs to do to reduce wasted efforts.

➢ The supervisor for the area needs to accurately plan how many operators are needed to produce the various levels of output that will be encountered in any of the production cells. This can be done by using the productivity calculation in reverse—factor in a realistic (i.e., demonstrated) productivity rate.

➢ Have a comprehensive list of job times (units per hour) for the entire operation so that individuals who slow down, either in their own cell or when seconded to a different cell, can be given some easily monitored targets for improvement.

➢ Do not forget that there are also productivity improvements to be made in improving operator morale and building ever more effective teams.

➢ Seek to encourage changes to product design, using fewer parts, quick to build, and mistake-proofed "design for manufacture" (DFM) assembly.

Chapter 8

Successfully Steering the Change Process

The Scale of the Task Ahead

Even though you may feel like a true lean disciple, don't think that you've got to be a superhero and personally implement every lean change on your own. It would be a futile gesture anyway, because one person dictatorially making all the changes will find that their efforts won't be permanent for very long. For long term acceptance and success, there needs to be widespread ownership for using the new lean production methods. Universal assent will never be achieved, so don't waste time and effort in seeking it. Instead, realize who the key influencers are, and ensure that they become committed to doing things lean. Gaining commitment can be achieved by getting these key influencers to buy into the lean plan by consulting them, and getting them to actively participate in implementing lean changes. This is an invaluable step in making the transformation a success. If you selfishly force actions on people because you arrogantly *think* you know more than they do (because you've read all the books), then you will meet a great deal of stubborn resistance, and you'll deserve it.

Getting to a state of being lean requires not only physical implementation work (moving benches and duplicating jigs and testers), but also a considerable change in the culture of the organization. The necessary changes in production philosophy will take time to come about, but are very important. So what are these changes in culture that are needed?

	Old Culture	Lean Culture
Quality	Quality is always up to someone else, rejects are a fact of life, never accept the blame for them.	I hate making rejects, it reflects on me and reduces our productivity score. I'm proud of our very low reject rates. I believe they can be reduced further if we work on it.
Mobility	I must look busy and keep my head down so the supervisor leaves me on "my" job.	When work builds up I must move to keep it flowing. Anyway, working on different jobs is normal in these cells.

(Table continued on next page)

	Old Culture	**Lean Culture**
Attitude	The only work area that matters is the area I work in.	Our cell performance is important, but it's also our duty to meet the demand needs of the downstream cells we feed.
Skills	I want to be *really good* at one thing, being a specialist gives me a sense of security.	I'm required to know all the jobs in my home cell and in my temporary cells.
Material	Why should I have to tell anyone when I am getting low on parts? I'm not paid enough for the responsibility. It's not my problem.	The two-bin and kanban systems maintenance helps keep us operational. They are our tools for telling us what needs replacing and what the urgencies and priorities are.
Productivity	I have low output days and nobody cares. I've told them what needs to be done but I'm ignored, I'll keep my suggestions to myself from now on.	We won't tolerate any problems that mess up our productivity score. When the team says something needs to be done, we are listened to and it is fixed.

The good news is that such changes in culture are attainable if management "acts lean" and doesn't just "talk lean." The bad news is that it takes a couple of years to happen to any significant degree.

What Would be the Ultimate in Lean Production?

• All the suppliers of material have been changed to new vendors who provide little-and-often deliveries (however, it takes time to develop new supplier relationships).

• Large proportions of production are virtually WIP free, without the operational problems that this would normally create.

• All employees have been indoctrinated to understand what is expected/ required of them, and are both able and motivated to achieve the necessary results.

• The customers have had time to experience the benefits of a very flexible, short-lead time supplier and, via the sales team, they now place smaller but more frequent orders that smooth the loading on the factory, and this works in harmony with our lean production methods.

But How Does the Organization Get There?

There are two lean implementation strategies to decide between. The Directors could decide to ignore all the "soft" issues and try to go for the ultimate in lean manufacturing design. Skipping as many intermediary stages as possible will get them there quicker. Or the "crawling" organization can take a little more time, learning to walk before finally attempting to run. It could take a little time to discover what techniques work best in which situations; it could invest sufficient time to retrain its employees; and it could allow time to properly develop the major changes involved such as material supply restructuring.

High Risk but Fast

The reason people want to pick this strategy is because of the temptation of large improvements being attained very quickly. The risk is (in fact it is a certainty) that although redesigning the shop floor with "U" shaped cells is relatively quick to do, everything else will lag behind: external and internal material supply systems, operations management culture, operator culture, supervisory culture, sales order processing systems, etc. My experience shows that you should not *even think* of risking it.

When this strategy fails, a lot of people will love to be able to say, "I knew it wouldn't work here," or "I told them so." Not only do you risk wasting all your efforts without making the gains you wanted, but any future lean changes will now have a bad taste associated with them because of the initial failure.

Far greater an issue would be the considerable risk that customer relations would be severely damaged, with much poorer levels of service being achieved than was possible when there were high inventories of finished goods. The customers might not wait around long enough for the organization to get things straightened out. The cost to the business for such a failure, if not crippling, would be catastrophic.

Low Risk but Slow

The reason for selecting this option is that there is so much to learn. Who will be the change agents, the lean disciples? Who are the influencers, who are planners, who are the doers? Which people on the shop floor will be ill-suited for working together effectively in cellular teams? Which lean techniques will work, and which won't, in each different part of the factory?

There is also so much to do. All medium and large sized companies have large numbers of products, people, components, processes, systems, suppliers, and customers. Many aspects of these will need to be altered to suit lean production. Even if it could all be changed to the required lean design in a matter of days without any mistakes or misjudgments, the people (i.e., the culture) would lag way behind. The business needs to develop its lean disciples, it needs to get some small wins under its belt first, to learn some of the techniques, to gain some confidence and credibility. It will take time to make people see that lean changes won't risk jobs but will instead actually increase long-term job security. A year or so after starting the implementations, operators will see that lean cells mean more job variety, increased skill levels, and that they create an environment of dynamism and empowerment.

One to two years to make all the changes necessary is not such a long time when everything is considered, as long as you don't take 5 years planning what to do before you actually move that first bench. Because Taiichi Ohno had no one to guide him, it took him many, many years to fully develop the Toyota Production System. However, because the culture had time to evolve, his evolutionary production system (revolutionary to the rest of the world) became a business philosophy for how Toyota would operate from then on.

The Order of Change Progression
At the outset, your business needs to appreciate the pattern of change that will be required, and it should set itself some milestones that it plans to pass along the way. Prior to putting in any cells, kanbans, or lineside delivery systems, there is plenty of preparation work that is highly advisable. A typical route that the lean journey should take might be as follows.

1. Make a significant "kaizen" effort on the shop floor. (Kaizen is a continuous structured incremental approach to improvement through the identification and elimination of waste.) Get key operators feeling empowered by giving them opportunities to say what needs to be improved, and showing them that their suggestions will be acted upon.

2. Start some small two-bin systems, replacing the need for such items as production route cards.

3. Begin evaluating employees to find out who shows aptitude for being a change agent on the shop floor and in production engineering.

4. Perform the value-added versus lead time analysis. Train "disciples" in the egg box and bristle block (or sticklebrick) games in-house (see the Appendix for descriptions of these games). The Production Manager, Materials Manager, Supervisors, and Production Engineers then need to discuss the lessons from these training games and the

opportunities within the factory for similar improvements. This will need to be organized and steered by the first lean disciple.

5. Implement the first minor kanban in an appropriate area, e.g., a family of subassemblies.

6. Plan the factory's first U-shaped cell. Perform "takt time" analysis. (Takt is the German word for an orchestra conductor's baton used to regulate the beat or timing of a performance. In lean production, it is the time required to complete a product, and it is discussed in detail in a later chapter.) Plan how to achieve work balancing, and design a bench layout to suit. There must be sufficient commitment provided to guarantee that this first cell will work.

7. Make "before" measurements, i.e., value-add time as a percentage of total lead time, space required, WIP inventory, productivity, reject rates, skill levels, housekeeping standards, and also remember to take "before" photos. These will all enable comparisons with the "after" results.

8. Now implement the first U-shaped cell quickly (within days), using the principles of the "Lean Leap." At the same time, make a big housekeeping improvement. Put in easy-to-use cell measures, and start a cross-skill training program.

9. Now monitor and coach the cell members to ensure that they work to the rules of multipiece flow or one-piece flow, whichever has been selected. Ensure that the team calculates its own quality and productivity rates, and hold cell meetings each week to review the team's performance and develop further improvements.

10. Perform a SMED workshop for the machine intensive "big batch" areas.

11. Analyze which product demand patterns make them kanbanable, and for which products this does not hold true. Agree on how to schedule those products that aren't kanbanable. For those that are, fully design the kanbans including tickets and boards.

12. Implement the full kanban systems for all the relevant assembly areas, so the replenishment of a moderately sized stock-holding rack occurs according to which product lines the packing area is using up to meet its daily dispatch requirements.

13. Perform second, third, fourth, etc., lean U-shaped cell implementations, learning more each time.

14. Get the materials stored lineside, as close to the cells that require

them as possible. While initially using a labor intensive check and replenish method to avoid stockouts, design and put into place, one by one, some autonomous/kanban replenishment systems to signal to the upstream batch process which materials need to be supplied and in what quantities. For externally supplied parts, put in simple "faxbans." (Faxbans combine the concept of kanban with the immediacy of the fax machine—production floor fax machines are used to let suppliers know when a resupply of parts or materials is required.)

15. Change the style of the production meeting away from target build numbers and toward keeping the kanbans out of the red (indicating a low supply of parts or materials) by moving labor to where needs are greatest. Use the meeting to monitor productivity and delivery performance, and to plan the necessary corrective actions to deal with problems.

16. Change the material supply chain systems and philosophies. Go further than the faxbans, design for smaller and more frequent deliveries. Bring in barcode-swiping material replenishment systems. Pinpoint the causes of material stockouts and systematically eliminate them—permanently.

17. Retrain sales staff. Arrange internally for large customer orders to be broken down into smaller ones. Develop a system of smooth loading the shop floor with work to reduce spikes in the demand pattern being passed on to the manufacturing system. Build relationships with the external customers to encourage smaller shipments that are more frequently placed.

18. Everything in the factory should be made "visual," including training sheets, components, and subassembly display boards, etc.

19. Now go for the ultimate lean system. Vertically merge cell "islands" as much as possible from subassembly through final assembly, and right through to packing, so that, apart from the initial batch processes, as many products as possible get assembled, tested, and packed with a lead time of single-figure hours.

20. Drive home the advantage of better delivery performance and responsiveness to win more business, and put more production cells into the space which was generated when the excess WIP and spaced-apart processes were changed into small U-shaped cells.

I have described the overall change process early in the book to lay the goundwork for what will follow. The size of the challenge and the order of change should now be much clearer. While reading the following chapters, everything should be viewed within the context of the "big picture" we have outlined to this point.

The Two-Day "Lean Leap" Cell Implementation Style

There is no reason that a well-designed and planned cell can't be implemented in a matter of two days. There is a saying that "you can't leap a canyon in two bounds," likewise, there is no point in half-implementing a U-shaped cell. It is an ideal opportunity to make a huge change in culture (self-performance measurement by operators) and in housekeeping standards. The advantages of doing it rapidly is that the pain of lost production is greatly reduced, and it demonstrates to everyone the commitment and potential behind this lean revolution.

Preparation

- Perform takt time analysis and operational line balancing. What jobs should be combined?

- Design the new cell, identifying with labels which of the current benches are going to be used as each of the future benches as they are positioned on the layout drawing.

- Purchase any new equipment needed for operators to quickly test their own work.

- Generate all the charts and cell performance measures, including the calculation sheets.

Day 1

- Clear the area, moving out any benches, shelves, or cabinets that will conflict with the new cell layout. At the same time, give everything a good cleaning.

- Dispose of all unnecessary items (obsolete jigs, fixtures, and tools). Also, take items that are only used occasionally and locate them in some other part of the shop where they can be easily found if and when they are required.

- Reorganize the benches and equipment into their new positions. Use enough people to ensure that the electrical supply, compressed air services, and extraction are reconnected as quickly as possible.

Day 2

- All the material and equipment that is always/regularly used needs to be stored on lineside shelving. Every item's storage container needs to show the correct part number, and every shelf location needs to be identified so that there is a specific place for each of the different lineside items.

- The boundaries of the cell and the cell's entrance (to show that it needs to be kept clear) need to be marked on the floor. Component bins need to be arranged to facilitate quick changeovers.

- The cell notice board needs to be located, and measurement charts pinned on it.

Work That Will be Ongoing

The performance calculations need to be delegated to the team; pick the most suitable person—perhaps the person who protests the least—who is confident working with figures. The cell members will need coaching for several weeks to ensure that they move around when required, so they realize when it is necessary to change over to a different product, and so they know how to organize themselves as circumstances change throughout the day. Regular cell meetings will help monitor and improve the quality and productivity standards by producing action plans for putting a training program in place, and getting all those minor physical adjustments to the cell to be carried out by engineering resources.

Know Where Your Problems Will Appear

Don't think that your main problems will be technical: lean manufacturing is relatively simple. No, the main problem will come from people who are resistant to change. Opposition *may* come in the form of a combination of the following types of people in management. These few examples are listed in order of significance.

The Faltering Operations/Production Director

Without his or her commitment, authority, and leadership, you might as well pack up and go home. The sanction of top-level management is a prerequisite. The lean methods change process is a middle- to long-term strategy. Many of the reasons for the changes go beyond pure accounting/business school logic but are, nonetheless, sound in theory and application. The Director may be faltering because he/she feels to be aging fast, approaching retirement, and is by now just biding their time. This type of person may be out of touch with the new technology, doesn't wish to rock the boat, and spends a lot of time looking over both shoulders for any possible rivals or reasons that could spell their replacement.

The Defensive

This is a middle manager who feels threatened by colleagues and the changes that they suggest—changes that are going to directly (or indirectly) affect their own department. The fear is that either extra work will be foisted upon them, or perhaps the opposite—that the work in their own department will be reduced. There is also a degree of criticism that is implied by such proposed changes, that what they've been doing for all these years has not been good enough. The hard work they've been putting in all these years is being thrown back in their face. There may also be some frustration that it wasn't the "defensive" who came up with the lean ideas; someone else has stolen his/her *potential* glory. Whatever the problem is, the defensive will actively wish to see the old, original methods reinstated to restore the comfort zone in which they feel in control, needed, and safe. Their hoped-for failure of the changes can't happen quickly enough.

The Doubting Cynic

The doubting cynic listens to everything that is going on around them and has time to go to all the meetings. He/she is careful not to say anything too negative in front of some people, but is highly critical when alone with the people that are willing to listen. The cynic wants to be able to say, "I told you so," and looks forward to finding it funny to see (what he/she perceives to be) another "management fad" fail.

The Self-Seeker

This manager isn't at work to work for the company. He/she is there to promote his/her own career. Every opportunity is taken to use the latest buzzwords. Colleagues will often keep lists of the ones he/she has as their current favorites. The risk is that this person will simply get in the way, making meetings far longer because they keep taking the focus off making improvement changes to get it back on themselves.

The Sponge

Not strong characters these people, and it is difficult to say what motivates them. Sponges are keen to go on a company visit and have free lunches. But back at the office they squirm and writhe to escape performing any (extra) work. Sometimes they will make such a slow or poor job of the things they are asked to do that the person who asked them will wish that they'd done it themselves. This type of person listens to everything, nods at the right times, and goes along with everything. At crucial points when you need sufficient mass/momentum to implement things and get actions to happen by the deadlines agreed, this person will end up letting everyone down, not maliciously but simply because of apathy.

Taking People With You

Management

The only way to get individual managers on your side is through education. Training courses are useful here but, sadly, many people will think that such theory sounds great, but imagines their company to be totally unique so it probably "won't work here." This is why a really powerful educational tool is to visit companies that are already using kanban and pull systems, which have cellular manufacture and systems for small and frequent material replenishment in place on the shop floor. Especially visit the companies that have processes, products, and sales volumes similar to your company. As long as they aren't competitors, try telephoning them to arrange it— you will find that they will rarely refuse—ask to be shown around by the lean disciple who personally put the kanban system in place, and who can personally provide qualified answers to your questions.

Shop Floor

You'll obviously need a lot of support from the operators. To get this, there must be considerable, not just token, involvement. Know who the key people are to get on your side, who will give good input into cell design, and who, if won over, will promote the changes to their colleagues. Likewise, know which people will spread negative influences (the shop floor cynics) and make sure they aren't involved in your first cells. Move them somewhere else in the factory; what you will really need are enthusiastic team people.

Don't waste time involving everyone with equal intensity—spreading energy too thinly in this way will be ineffective. But do make sure you brief everyone who will be affected so that no one can say they've been ignored or kept in the dark. Once the momentum of lean implementation has begun on the shop floor, the majority of operators can be swept along on the wave of the changes if they are kept involved and are always treated with consideration.

Supervision

It would be unrealistic to expect long-serving leading hands or supervisors to come up with, or easily adopt, lean ideas and the new production philosophies. Years of knowledge and experience of traditional factory methods, which seem intuitively correct, cannot be erased overnight. Training and coaching will be required for them, and it might not come easy. The supervisors will be people who will be doing some of the implementation but are not going to be the ones directing it. Do not make the assumption that supervisors will be able to drive the changes forward, as they are often too focused on getting product to customers. Only managers with higher levels of authority, who have been educated in lean and are also highly motivated (lean disciples), will be able to drive forward the changes.

The key point about supervision is that at this level of management it is very, very important to get it right if the changes are to be maintained. Getting it wrong will almost guarantee a slip back to the old ways. If you can't develop the existing supervisors into the required type of people, one option will be to restructure and hire (possibly younger) people with the right backgrounds and with lots of enthusiasm. It is always best for the business to try and grow its own people into these roles because new externally acquired employees will face too much of a learning curve to come to grips with the factory's products, processes, and part numbers. New supervisors will also take up to a year before they get to understand their own team of people and truly gain some trust and respect from them.

Chapter 9

Factory and Cell Design

The Design of a Traditional Factory

The factory design shown in **Figure 9.1** represents a traditional macrolayout that is repeated (approximately) in many, many companies. Two different product/markets are typical, whether defense/civil aircraft parts, food/ other sheet plastics, dairy/sports rubber moldings, automotive/office air conditioning units, etc. For a company to concentrate on just one market or product is normally too risky, so a second market is found whose products can be made using the same types of initial processing equipment. Then the factory is split into some focused areas dedicated to those different product markets.

The initial, secondary, or tertiary production processes will be made up of large, capital-intensive pieces of equipment that will likely run on a double-days, 24-hour rotating or continental shift working pattern. Such areas might be material mixing/processing, blow molding or extrusion lines, calendering lines, stamping presses, machining centers, injection molding presses, surface-mount PCB lines, etc.

The materials that feed these areas are bought in bulk on a weekly or monthly basis for purchasing and transport economies. This requires a

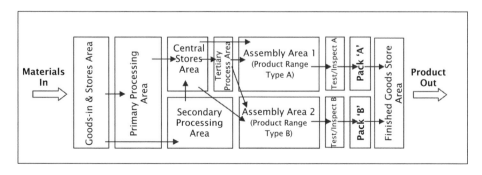

Figure 9.1. Example of a typical factory layout.

substantial goods-in-storage area prior to the shift working sections. After these initial large batch processes, there is likely to be an intermediary/central storage facility. This also needs to be large because the primary processes running shifts are not only processing large batches, but the material is being consumed over a shorter work period by the downstream areas, who will often be only working a normal day pattern.

Downstream of the central stores area, there are dedicated areas for assembling the product ranges, and thus completing the build work. Traditionally, a final-inspection and test department, manned by dedicated indirect inspectors who hold sway over whether or not the product meets the required standards, follows. The penultimate stage is packing, and finally there is a finished-goods store. The FG store is also large because either the shipments being sent out are large, and it takes time to accumulate the full order quantities; or the area is used as a buffer to ensure that customers receive a good service of delivery performance. In the latter instance, the next month's build targets might then be based on replenishing the stores back to the agreed stocking levels, so the FG stores also serve to drive the planning process.

Lack of Teamwork

The functional layout lends itself to a functional supervisory structure where different supervisors are responsible for each separate area. Usually they have different goals and targets, and they are always more concerned about their own problems than anyone else's. This leads to inefficiencies, as operators that stay in one department will fail to understand the whole process, and supervisors and managers will eventually become rivals rather than colleagues. Even the different teams of shift workers within a department will bicker over issues of material replenishment, housekeeping, work cherry picking, and which shift is trying to avoid doing difficult setups at the expense of the next.

Inventory

In WIP heavy systems, the material flow (as already discussed) is ponderously slow. The sheer volume requires immense and very detailed stock-check counts every 6 to 12 months in order for the finance people to know how many hundreds of thousands of dollars are tied up in inventory. More frequent but generalized monthly stock checks will also be carried out to organize the short term planning of the whole factory. Computer solutions, such as MRP, are then needed to process all this information and organize material replenishment schedules.

Piecework

If piecework incentives are prevalent, then we have another issue that will cause problems. Operators will fudge their build numbers, work will be hidden or held back for rainy days, performance levels will sit at the levels operators think are financially optimal for them, and rise no higher. Also, workers will resist changing jobs because they will lose their bonus until they gradually get up to speed. There is a risk that the times on the next job are a lot harder than the present one; so even though it is boring, it is better to stay on the same job for years on end. Quality takes a distant second place to quantity, and the urge to keep building product, whether it's needed or not, is very strong.

The Traditional Assembly Area Microlayout

Let's take a closer look at the way product is traditionally assembled. The usual layout will be as functional as possible, utilizing lots of straight lines and long conveyors, with rows of benches organized in either one of two ways, as shown in **Figure 9.2**.

There are parochial advantages to this. Each operator can have his or her own bench with a lockable drawer, and is able to modify their chair's cushions for comfort. There is no need to move material excessively because

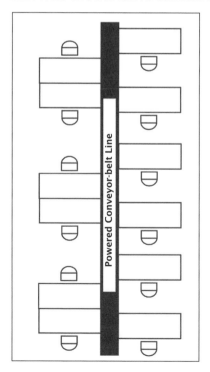

Figure 9.2. Example of traditional bench arrangements.

the conveyor belt moves it along at a controlled rate. As long as materials are supplied throughout the day, the supervisor can leave the operators on the same job all day, or until the piles of WIP indicate that a particular job needs to be stopped for a while. If piecework bonuses are in operation, the supervisor's job of calculating the bonus rates is made easier if people don't move on to different jobs too frequently.

A Pair of Paradigms

Straight lines and functional layouts are a result of a paradigm. A paradigm is an archetype (a model that is copied for all similar needs) that limits change and constrains innovation, and keeps people from thinking laterally.

As an example, two of the biggest paradigms of factory layouts are the following.

1. It is best to keep the main assembly operation as close to the dispatch end as possible to reduce handling.

2. Because factories are usually big rectangular buildings where materials enter at one end and finished products are shipped from the other, all material must travel from one end to the other. Straight lines represent the shortest route between two points, so straight lines and conveyors are the best design for production lines in factories.

Both these statements are almost always wrong; but, being paradigms, everyone believes them to be true.

Paradigm 1: *Production Should be Closer to Finished Products Than to Incoming Goods*

The almost universally held belief that it is best to get as much of production as close to the dispatch department as possible, as shown in **Figure 9.3**, is false.

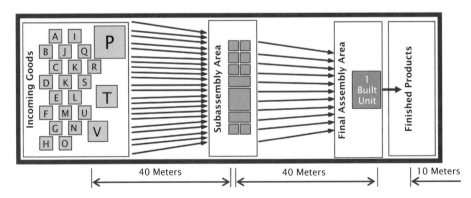

Figure 9.3. Distances traveled by parts in a traditional factory.

As shown, the cumulative unit travel distance in this traditional factory = $(23 \times 40) + (11 \times 40) + (1 \times 10)$. This totals a considerable 1,370 meters.

It is far more appropriate to have lineside storage, as shown in **Figure 9.4**, of components and not worry too much about assembling the product a long way from the finished goods store because the cumulative parts travel distance is far less: $(23 \times 20) + (1 \times 70) = 530$ meters.

Completing the build of a product as quickly as possible in its inevitable journey from incoming goods to the other end of the factory (finished goods) is also far better in terms of double-handling, and the volumes of space taken up by parts on the shop floor. Again, if proof is required, count out all the components and materials needed to build 100 products into some tubs and trays, and compare the volume they take up to that of 100 finished and packed units. A good estimate is that they will take up twice the volume or floor space.

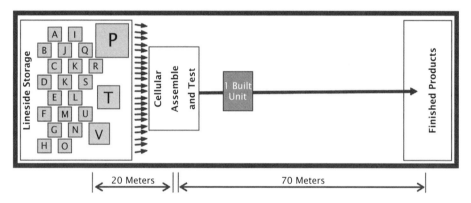

Figure 9.4. Proof that lean assembly cells are best sited close to incoming goods.

Paradigm 2: *Straight Lines Are Always Best*

This second paradigm statement is also false. Straight lines are not always ideal in factories—whether on a macroscale or in cells. The rest of this chapter will explain why smaller benches and "U" shaped cells are optimal.

Ergonomics and the Traditional Work Bench

Human body movement does not handle straight lines very well. When we walk or run, our feet follow curved loops. When we swat a fly or wipe a window clean, our hands follow curved paths. An entertainer who imitates a "robot-man," where the majority of his movements are in straight lines, is captivating to an audience because it looks so alien and demonstrates the performer's extreme control of limb motion. In fact, if we ask human arms

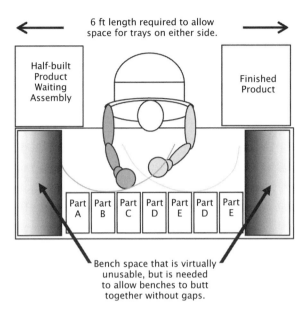

Figure 9:5. Inefficient use of space using a traditional six-foot bench.

to push/pull things in straight lines, we make things very awkward. **Figure 9.5** shows how inefficient the traditional work bench is.

Making it Easier for Assembly Operators

Ideally, it is always better for movements to be small and for the reaching distances to be minimal. Double handling (out of one box and into another) is not only wasted time but increases the risk of manual-handling strain. Boxes or trays of work on either side of an operator's chair also make it awkward to get in and out, and will necessitate big benches to avoid gaps between adjacent benches through which work could fall. However, the reach limit of an individual means that a large proportion of such a bench is unusable (except for storage, which is not a value-adding function). These portions of surface are then available for clutter, such as electric fans, personal bags, etc., leading to poor standards of housekeeping.

Big benches and lots of boxes beside each operator take up lots of valuable space. This arrangement also prevents operators from being able to pass work on to each other. One of the simplest lessons that the bristle block (or sticklebrick) game (see the Appendix for details) teaches is that it is quite possible for four people to get around one small table to perform the value-adding work.

The traditional layout shown in **Figure 9.6**, using 6 ft × 2 $^1/_2$ ft benches, requires 144 ft² of floor space including an allowance for

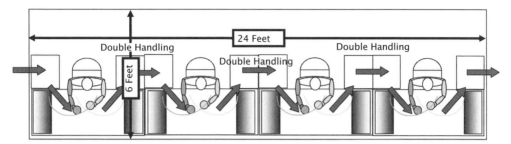

Figure 9.6. How inefficiently used space builds up in a traditional workspace.

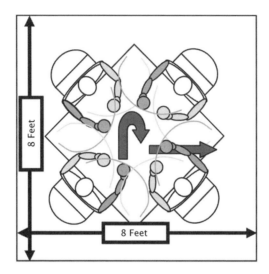

Figure 9.7. How a lean workbench can use far less space.

operators to get in and out of their workstations.

The bristle block variation (the operator models, *though not to scale*, are in proportion) seen in **Figure 9.7** uses a 4 ft × 4 ft bench, and the whole area it requires is 64 ft^2 of floor space.

Even if this 55% reduction in space example *seems* too far-fetched, space savings of 40–60% *are truly achievable* in such assembly areas (it has been done many times), especially when spare "just-in-case" equipment, benches, and excess WIP are removed.

Optimizing Bench Size and Layout

If you have an assembly process that involves trays/boxes of WIP, you will need to space your benches apart, or you will need unnecessarily long (6 ft) benches. When designing a lean, low-WIP system, using one-piece flow and smaller 4 foot benches becomes not only possible *but necessary*—adjacent operators would be spaced too far apart otherwise. Clearly, the square 4 ft × 4 ft bench used for the bristle block example is not necessarily appropriate but other alternatives should be considered.

Modern Cellular Bench Design

As discussed, human ergonomics are not linear—the movements our arms make around a stationary torso are curved. Add a small degree of body movement (helped by a rotating chair to avoid potential for back strain—see **Figure 9.8**) and the useable work area that is defined forms the shape of an arc. So perhaps the ideal bench should be an arc?

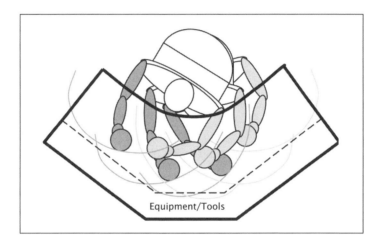

Equipment/Tools

Figure 9.8. A curved bench is more ergonomic.

The U-Shaped Cell

The logical progression from one isolated segment of arc, to having a small team of people working together in a cell, is to increase the arc so it becomes a U shape or a J shape. This doesn't necessarily mean throwing out all your old benches and buying new ones at great expense; such an expensive proposal should be dismissed immediately. You can be sensible with money by modifying the benches you have. By removing the worktops, the bench framework underneath can be shortened by cutting, then rewelded or bolted back together. New MDF or plywood worktops can be made to the size and shape needed, then varnished or melamine coated at minimal cost and bolted down onto the modified frame base.

To create the U shape without leaving gaps, add triangular melamine segments and support them between adjacent benches with brackets. For a deluxe look, cut new bench tops to include the triangular part so the

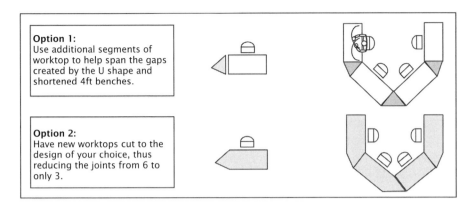

Option 1:
Use additional segments of worktop to help span the gaps created by the U shape and shortened 4ft benches.

Option 2:
Have new worktops cut to the design of your choice, thus reducing the joints from 6 to only 3.

Figure 9.9. How curved workbenches can be formed into a U-shaped cell.

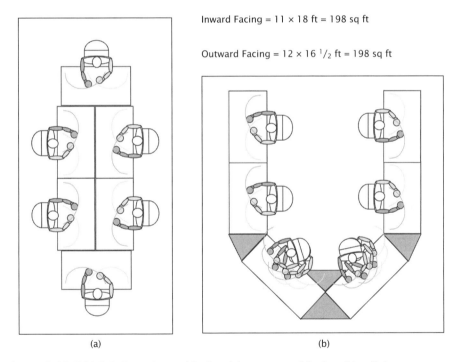

Inward Facing = 11 × 18 ft = 198 sq ft

Outward Facing = 12 × 16 $^1/_2$ ft = 198 sq ft

(a)   (b)

Figure 9.10. Which is best: inward facing (a) or outward facing (b) cells?

number of joins is reduced, but make sure you get the measurements, angles, and orientations right! See **Figure 9.9**.

The Alternative to a U-Shaped Cell

There are two options when getting people and benches closer together: the outward-facing U-shaped cell and the inward-facing O-shaped cell.

The left-hand cell in **Figure 9.10(a)** looks more compact, but the boundary space required for operators to get out of their chairs and move around the cell's outside is greater than one might think, especially when a limited amount of space for materials is provisioned. The cell in **Figure 9.10(b)** will need space located for parts, so it ends up taking the same amount of space as its inverted cousin.

There are more options for the flow of work in the inward facing cell: up, down, across, around, whereas the outward facing U-shape cell defines the flow of work in one of two possible directions around the cell—clockwise or counterclockwise.

Further Considerations

Making Cells People-Friendly

As long as the operators are close enough to pass work to each other without reaching, both setups have their merits. Try one of each and make up your own mind. I personally feel that the outward-facing U shape allows the kanban/notice board to be kept close to the work area without getting in the way. Take care because your eagerness to make the cell as small and cozy as possible (e.g., by using 3-ft-long benches) may make it very restricted for operators to get in and out of. Be sensible and always consider how you would like to work in the cell. What looks on a drawing to be adequate room can often be inadequate in practice, as shown in **Figure 9.11**.

The cell can be designed with the fastest operations having two duplicate benches in the cell, so a cell with 6 benches might only contain 3 different

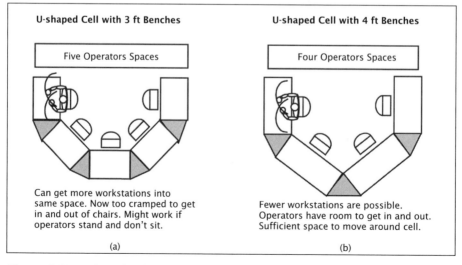

Figure 9.11. U-shaped cells can become *too* cramped.

operations, with each one having two benches on which to perform the work. The permutations are highly variable to suit the build activities that are encountered.

Services

The boundaries of the U-shaped cell are clearly defined, and if vanity boards (painted the color of the cell) are added, all the services can be hidden away nicely, and the result is a very tidy appearance. The services are easier to install in an O-shaped, inward-facing cell, as they only need to run along the center; but the overall appearance can end up looking quite cluttered. Even with an inward-facing cell, some operators may request vanity boards centrally underneath the cluster of benches, making service provision more complicated than initially envisioned.

When putting in a new bench layout and supplying the necessary services, wherever possible avoid bolting anything down to the floor. The culture of the organization needs to become one where change is not only accepted, it is expected and welcomed. Expect that you will want to move the cell around and modify it every 12 months or so.

Fire Evacuation

Fire officers would prefer to see the inward-facing cells because, for evacuation purposes, it is easier for operators to leave the cell; but the objection is a minor one. In fact, the inward-facing cell has greater potential for trolleys and boxes to be crowded around it, and this will hamper the movement of people even more. As long as both cells store their materials tidily, neither has a problem in allowing people quick movement away from the area and out of the building. If small cells like these are linked together, then even greater health and safety considerations are necessary. Always make provisions for this in cell designs.

Allowing for Flexibility in the Manning of Cells

A common misconception is that there needs to be an operator sitting at every chair/position in the cell. It *can* happen, but it should be extremely rare in practice. This scenario is only effective when all the operations can be truly balanced, otherwise it is decidedly ineffective. As you get nearer to totally filling the cell with people, you will find there is a fall-off in productivity. Even if perfect balancing is achieved, as soon as one person leaves the cell momentarily, either the whole team grinds to a halt (one-piece flow), or part of the team grinds to a halt and WIP builds up in front of the vacant chair. Can a leading hand fill in for the individual needing to leave the cell? Can the work balancing ever be fine-tuned to this degree? Will one or two individuals unfairly get their adjacent colleagues to take on a disproportionate amount of the work that they should be able to undertake themselves?

All of these pitfalls make true continuous one-piece flow in a multiperson cell of 4 or more people virtually unachievable, despite the ideals that you may now be aspiring to. Efficient one-piece flow (with few losses caused by out-of-balance waiting by operators) is elementary with a one-operator cell; with two operators it is highly feasible; with three it requires excellent teamwork and understanding, otherwise, it loses productivity. With more than three operators, one-piece flow can become more trouble than it is worth.

Therefore, a U-shaped cell with 6 workstations is best married with 3–4 people moving frequently from bench to bench, working with very small transfer batches enabling continuous (not one-piece) flow by the action of them chasing the work around the cell.

With this style of working, the cell's 6 operations are required to be only approximately balanced, and buildups of 6–12 pieces of work are allowed between adjacent benches—you decide whatever transfer batch quantity is appropriate. If an operator at the end of the cell runs out of work, he/she moves to an empty workstation at the start of the cell. If an operator at the start of the cell has built up their maximum transfer batch quantity, he/she must move to an unmanned downstream workstation to process the buildups of work to be found there. In this way, small ripples of work flow around the cell, pushed by flexible and mobile cell members.

When the kanban board for the cell indicates that production output rates need to be reduced, you are then faced with the question of what to do. If you leave all the operators where they are, the risk is that they will slow down because they can see that their kanban is full and the team's productivity level falls. In a multiperson cell of four people, the best option is to reduce the headcount by just one or two operators, reallocating them to cells whose kanbans are struggling to keep up with demand. But it might not be too much of a problem to close the cell entirely.

If the cell is a particularly large one (e.g., 8 operators/12 workstations), the option of closing the cell entirely should be avoided. Finding work for one or two people who are taken out of a cell is no problem at all. Finding jobs all at once for 6–10 people is a big headache. Therefore, if a big cell needs to be slowed down, decide this early and reduce it to up to half of its normal manning level.

During overtime working, it is often best to put the few operators that remain into one cell whose kanban needs urgent replenishment, rather than letting them go to their normal cells to work on their own, achieving very little in the process.

Cells Using Shared Resources

U-shaped cells are the building blocks for the organization to relayout large areas of the factory to start the lean revolution. But what happens when several of these U-shaped cells all need to use a shared resource such as a powder coating line or a flow solder bath?

The U-shaped cells can be placed either down both sides of a shared resource (as shown in **Figure 9.12**), or just on one side.

If you look at the top left cell in **Figure 9.12**, you can see how U-shaped cells can still function as unbroken processes, but with one of their operations (in this case, Op 3, flow soldering) being done outside of the cell.

Where necessary, a roving paint line operator/flow solder operator will be required to fetch work needing to go through the shared resource, and to bring it back once it has been processed. To signal which cells need to be serviced by the roving operator, one bench in each cell gets fitted with a doorbell button to trigger one of a series of lights directly above the shared operation. There is a different colored light to represent each of the four

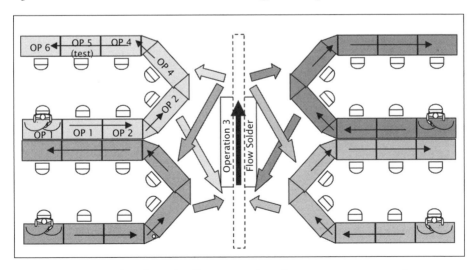

Figure 9.12. Several U-shaped cells may need to share a common operation.

cells. When the button is pressed, the respective light comes on and perhaps it also activates a short burst of noise from a buzzer (or perhaps not, for humane reasons). The shared-resource operator then knows which cell needs its work processing, and can cancel the light by pressing one of four buttons at his or her machine while leaving the lights on at any cell that still needs attention.

This system will need an electrician of some ability to put together. If this is too complicated or a quicker solution is required, then a series of colored flags can be used. An operator inside the U shape can put the flag up on a stand on top of the bench if it has work that is ready to be collected. Battery-operated doorbells can be used to avoid the need for wiring and relays.

Chapter 10

Two-Bin Systems and Basic Kanbans

Before a factory starts to use kanban systems, which can take some time to fully appreciate and comprehend, it is a good first step to implement some of the simpler autonomous replenishment techniques. This will help operators and managers to start putting their trust in something other than production plans or job/route cards that are prevalent as traditional methods of instructing areas on what to build and in what quantities. It is getting more and more popular to try to computerize any new system, as well as many existing ones. Many people will suggest that the simple replenishment methods about to be described are inferior to getting a computer to work it all out. This is a very dubious suggestion; things should *always* be kept as simple and as accessible as possible for both the operators and supervisors. Two-bin systems are simple, cheap, and quick to set up. Computer systems are expensive, complicated, unreliable, and take time to install.

In any factory, there are many applications where uncomplicated replenishment solutions would be appropriate, and once these are implemented the effort spent in counting WIP and writing out build instructions can begin to be reduced. The benefits in doing this early on in the journey toward leanness are that it will:

1. pave the way for people to understand full-blown kanbans and pull systems,

2. start reducing any unnecessary manual planning (and opportunities for stockouts), and

3. start empowering operators and leading hands to control their own areas.

Replenishment of Small Consumable Items

There are dozens of situations where tubs or trays of nuts, bolts, springs, screws, etc., need to be replenished on a regular basis. Two simple options are available to accomplish this, and either will result in making any parts that need to be reordered stand out clearly on the stocking shelves.

1. At points in the day, operators need to refill their workbench component containers from a nearby parts store. The tubs within this store, when more than half-full, are positioned on the shelves facing forward, with the front of the tubs being green in color. In contrast, the rear of the tubs is red in color. If, in the course of filling up the workbench containers, an employee lowers the level of one of these main storage tubs to *less* than half-full, that person knows he/she has the responsibility to turn that particular tub around on the shelf so that the red side shows. This makes it clearly stand out from the others. Green tubs indicate to everyone that stock quantities for the parts they contain are sufficient, but any tubs with the red end facing forward flags the materials that need to be requisitioned. Each day, the person responsible for reordering the items in that particular storage facility identifies any new boxes that have been turned around in addition to those already listed from the previous day, and places an order with the supplier for more of those components. When the parts come in, the tubs that can be refilled are turned around again to once more show green (see **Figure 10.1**).

2. In a situation where the tub is fixed and cannot be rotated around (e.g., it is clipped onto a louvered panel), make a double-sided card with one side green and one side red, and fit the card into the slotted front of the tub. The card is turned around when more components need to be reordered.

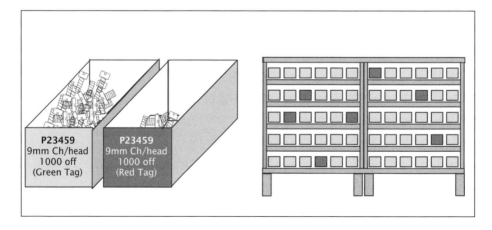

Figure 10.1. Simple two-bin system for replenishing small consumable items.

Further Refinements

It may be better to have a tub with a divider fixed across the middle to provide a separate front and rear compartment, or to use a larger tub inside which two smaller inner boxes can fit. This will result in less guessing about when the quantity of components has been reduced to half and, therefore, when the red card needs to be shown. Empty the front end first and when you need to start using parts from the back end of the box, the red signal needs to be shown. Once there are two storage compartments available, you now have what is known as a *two-bin system*. These work best when the quantity of safety-stock components kept in the red end of the tub can be accurately defined, and this is easiest to achieve when the components are supplied in bags or boxes of a known quantity.

If the components are supplied in bags of a fixed quantity, then leave them in their bags and ask operators to have only one of the multiple bags in the storage tub open at one time. Then you will be able to specify a very precise point for the tub to be turned around. State this on the tub along with the part number, e.g., "Reorder Point = less than 3 *whole* bags of 100 units each."

Even for this simple system to work there will need to be training and cooperation from every employee who comes into contact with this replenishment system.

Replenishment of Printed Labels

Some items are not readily stored in tubs or boxes: for example, rolls of labels or tape. These are best stored hung from bars attached to a louvered panel, as shown in **Figure 10.2**. Such hanging bars need safety attachments

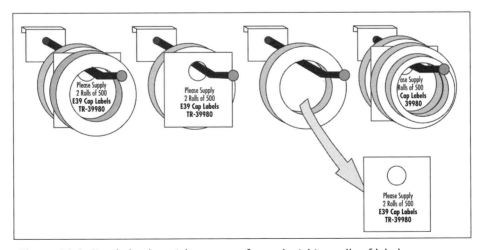

Figure 10.2. Simple kanban ticket system for replenishing rolls of labels.

fixed to their protruding ends to prevent personal injury or damage to clothing.

When the outer roll is taken, the kanban card is exposed and the leading hand in the section gives it to the label-making department. The second roll (behind the kanban card) is there as safety stock to prevent a stockout while the next rolls are being sourced. For stock rotation, any partial rolls are stored at the front, and one *full* roll (or whatever is deemed necessary) is kept behind the card so there is sufficient safety stock while the replenishment process is occurring.

Replenishment of Printed Covers

Some items such as bulky plastic moldings have to be stored in large boxes. This presents a set of circumstances different from those encountered with small components.

For the purposes of this example, the end products in question are a range of electronically operated control boxes, the cover moldings for which are pad-printed with details such as model type, the display features, and the button functions. In this instance, there are up to 40 different product variants to be accommodated. Traditionally, a production planner would inspect the stock of printed covers each week and issue job-card instructions on what covers need printing over the next five days. Prior to the kanban improvement, the cover moldings would be printed in batches of 4 boxes at a time, each box containing 120–140 printed covers. Despite these large quantities, there are inevitably several occasions each week when last-minute panic printing is required, partly because the print operators tend to cherry-pick the easiest print jobs first, avoiding the awkward variants for as long as possible.

This is a situation where a simple kanban ticket replenishment system can be utilized so that stock levels of printed covers can be greatly reduced and, at the same time, out-of-stock occurrences can be eliminated. In a lean system, it would be preferable to hold just one box of each of the printed variants and have only a modest amount of stock kept as blank molded covers—perhaps just 10 to 30 full boxes. The pad printing operation is already quite flexible and has plenty of spare capacity. The printed covers are being consumed on a little-and-often basis, and in a lean replenishment system you would no longer want there to be the need for constant stock checking to be performed by supervisors.

1. One box of 100 XYZ printed covers sits in a defined place "lineside" the assembly cell along with the ~40 other types.

2. Gradually, as that variant gets assembled to fulfill the different build mixes each day, the level of printed covers within the box drops.

3. When there is only one day's worth of covers left, the XYZ kanban card is put in the kanban card rack located centrally in the pad-printing area.

4. 100 XYZ covers are printed and taken over. Any remaining covers from the previous batch are put on top. The card is also returned with the full box to the lineside store.

Large 5" × 5" kanban tickets are created, one for each of the individual printed cover variants. They are designed to be stuck to the boxes using Velcro patches. The rules of the kanban are that when an operator sees that the number of printed covers in a box falls below ~30 (less than one-quarter full), the kanban card is removed from that box and is given to the printing department. It is explained to the operators that they are fully responsible for ensuring that this happens, and failure to carry out this step will risk customer shipments being made incomplete or late.

Each kanban ticket received by the printing section is a request that 100 covers of that specific variant be printed. When this has been done, the box of printed covers (100 units will only 80% fill a box) is delivered to the cell together with the attached kanban card. There should still be several printed covers of the same type that remain in the original box. To avoid having more than one container for any one printed cover, these are then placed on top of the new batch, which is why the new box wasn't filled right to the top.

The printing department stores any kanban cards that are waiting to be printed in a card rack, the type of rack that is commonly used to store employee clock cards. The leading hand of the assembly department, being the customer, arranges the cards in the order that he/she wishes them printed, the most urgent ones being placed at the top. With this card rack, everyone can see both what priorities exist and what the print section's overall workload is. If there are a large number of kanban tickets, it indicates that there may be too few print operators. If there are only one or two tickets, it may be appropriate to reduce the manning level in the section and transfer the manpower to a more needy area.

Replenishment of Electrical Connection Leads

Some items such as electrical connection leads are best kept in bundles of an agreed quantity. This keeps them from getting tangled and makes it

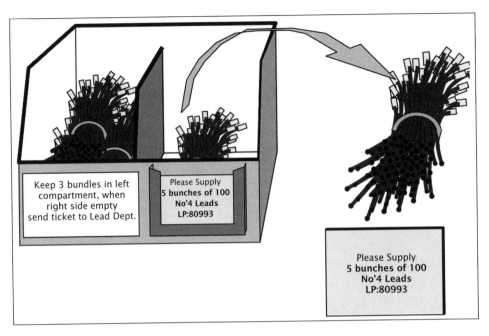

Keep 3 bundles in left compartment, when right side empty send ticket to Lead Dept.

Please Supply
5 bunches of 100
No'4 Leads
LP:80993

Please Supply
5 bunches of 100
No'4 Leads
LP:80993

Figure 10.3. Simple kanban system for replenishing bundles of leads.

easier to keep track of them. In this example, a removable kanban card gets sent to the section that produces the leads at a clearly determined point, e.g., when the stock falls below a specified limit. The rules for this are best stated on the front of the storage container so that there is no ambiguity. The point at which the card gets removed doesn't necessarily have to be when the stock falls to half the maximum. A two-bin system can be set to whatever quantities and whatever rules are most appropriate. In the example shown in **Figure 10.3**, three bundles are always kept on the left-hand side of the tub. When the first of these left-hand bundles has to be taken, then that is the point at which the reorder card gets sent to the lead section who is then required to produce and deliver five bundles as soon as possible. Again, when the bundles are dropped off, the kanban card gets returned to the slot in the front of the tub.

Experiment with this reorder point level of stock to find the minimum quantity it can be set to, so that even in a particularly busy period of demand the downstream cell doesn't quite run out altogether.

Chapter 11

Moderately Simple Kanban Systems

Simple replenishment systems do not necessarily have to be one-bin or two-bin types. There are frequent situations where larger components have to be stored in appropriately large containers such as tote boxes, trays, etc., in sufficient quantities for there to be *multiple* bins needed to keep the assembly operation adequately supplied. Nevertheless, as a lean practitioner you still want an uncomplicated replenishment system to control the resupply of these materials. This is ideal for a simple kanban solution.

Kanbans are an excellent way to link different production areas together. They ensure the effective replenishment of materials and also prevent the overproduction of components by visually setting out defined limits for holding stocks.

Due to the degree of capital invested in machines and machine tools, operations using high cost capital equipment are usually run for either 16- or 24-hour periods each day. In contrast, labor-intensive operations are likely to be performed on single day shifts to keep shift-premium costs to a minimum. At best, over half the daily output from a shift working area will have to go directly into storage containers rather than immediately feeding a day-working cell. As such, this is a typical multiple bin storage situation. With two adjacent manufacturing operations (machinery-intensive on two shifts, manual assembly on 8-hour days) being run so differently, connecting the demands of one to the replenishment priorities of the other is, therefore, best achieved using a multiple-ticket kanban system.

Kanbans that link primary operations—such as those linking multishift working machinery-intensive areas to the day-shift working assembly areas immediately downstream—can often be relatively straightforward to create if the situation is simple. In such cases, you can normally get away with common sense to determine how large the maximum kanban stocks should be for each of the different types of materials/parts.

Replenishing Subassembly Parts

Two-bin systems won't work in all cases. For example, let's examine an assembly area whose products use large brass electrical terminals in moderately high volumes. They cannot use a two-bin system because the weight of the brass and the quantities involved would make the bins too heavy. Before going lean, the storage method was as follows. The various bins were located on some shelves a short distance away from the assembly area. The bins were usually filled to levels that were unsafe for anyone other than a strong man to carry. Their storage positions on the shelves were often indeterminate because neither their required shelf location nor their part numbers were clearly identified. It was common that once a week one or more of the terminal types would slip unnoticed down to a zero stock holding level, necessitating the leading hands to panic and expedite a new batch of the unavailable terminal through to the assembly area as quickly as possible.

First, the weight of the laden bins had to be limited for safe lifting practice to no more than 8 kg, making it necessary to only *partially* fill the bins; but this meant that the total number of available bins would need to be increased to prevent the assembly department from running out of terminals. Therefore, a simple kanban was designed to make the stock-holding levels and replenishment priorities for each terminal far more visible and reliable. It was also an opportunity to position the storage closer to lineside and improve the housekeeping of the area at the same time.

To decide the maximum number of bins needed for the terminals, two things had to be determined for each individual part number: 1) the number of terminals in a bin that make up a gross weight that is safe to lift, i.e., ~8 kg, and 2) the typical weekly consumption rates for the different terminals. With this knowledge, it was then possible to decide on some sensible stock holding quantities.

Previously, the shelves had not been a good way to store the bins because they did not clearly position each different component in a specific and fixed location. However, since the design of the bins allows them to conveniently stack on top of one another, it was possible to make stacks of bins part of the kanban itself. Here is how the system was redesigned. The first step was to replace the shelves with two large pieces of white melamine board: one to form a backboard against which the kanban design would be arranged, and the other to be used as a floorboard onto which the bins would be positioned in fixed locations without the floor having to be affected (e.g., painted) in the process. The floorboard would also prevent the floor material being scuffed as bins were moved around. Knowing the size of the bins, and what the maximum height that each stack would be, allowed the right quantity of correctly sized pieces of red, yellow, and green laminated card to be made up and then fixed onto the backboard as shown in **Figure 11.1**.

It was appreciated that each stack of bins would need to be kept separated and orientated in a standardized way. In order to grasp a bin from the top of any stack, there would also need to be enough space between the bin and the backboard to allow the front and back handles to be grasped without one's knuckles getting bashed. By attaching wooden battens to the floorboard between and also behind the bins (keeping a 4" gap around them), enough space was provided so that the handles could then be reached safely. The battens positioned between the bins also ensured that the stacks would be kept in a location and orientation that was fixed. Above each of the stacks on the backboard the essential information was presented—the part numbers, descriptions, and kanban quantities. Also, pictures of the terminals themselves were included.

The principle behind the red, yellow, and green colors that are used in a kanban board design is based on the colors used in a traffic light system. With a kanban, red is a warning, yellow is a caution, and green means "no problem." A maximum number of containers equally proportioned between each of the three colors is required for the kanban to work properly. If there are only two bins, (which I would advise is not really sufficient) one should be red and the other green. If there is an even number of four or more, the split-quantities of the kanban colors can be left to personal preference.

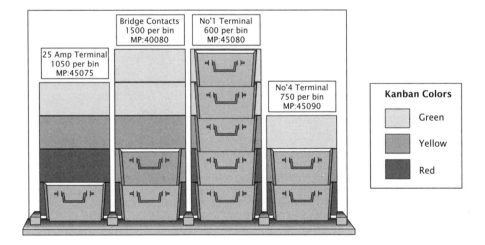

Figure 11.1. Kanban system for replenishment of brass terminals.

To stay in touch with changes in demand from the downstream product assembly area, the leading hand of the metal-preparation section now simply has to keep a watchful eye on the kanban board as deliveries are made. The replenishment priorities are determined by how far up the kanban pattern of colored squares the stack reaches. If red is revealed, replenishment of that part is a very high priority. Yellow indicates medium priority, and green a low priority. The cumulative height of the colored cards serves to limit the total number of bins in a stack. Additionally, as with all kanbans, if *all* the stacks of bins are in the red, it suggests that more people need to be added to the metal-preparation section because they must be struggling to keep up with demand. However, if the bins are *all* in the green, then people can be released from the metal preparation section and transferred to other departments that need additional labor.

Replenishment of Surface-Mount PCBs

The "lab" rack is a common way to store printed circuit boards (pcbs), and the type shown in **Figure 11.2** holds a maximum of 160 SMT (surface-mount technology) built pcb panels.

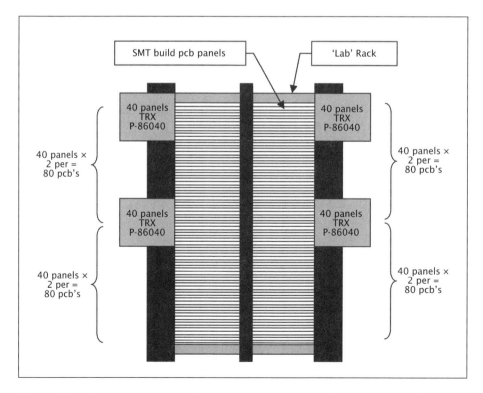

Figure 11.2. Lab rack being used as a kanban container of surface mounted printed circuit boards.

When pcbs are relatively small, 2, 3, 4, or more individual boards are designed into a single 12" × 5" sheet or panel, a size that, in this example, is standard for the SMT line. This is a practical panel size to use because it allows the surface mount machine to work effectively, and reduces the amount of handling needed by the operators. These panels get separated into individual pcbs at a later point. In **Figure 11.2**, there are two pcbs per panel, so a full rack holds 160 panels or 320 pcbs. The kanban tickets are attached by using Velcro.

In the kanban system example shown in **Figure 11.3**, there are seven different types of pcbs being produced by the SMT area. Three are for use in an Orange assembly cell, three for use in a Purple cell, and just one pcb type is supplied for use in a Blue cell.

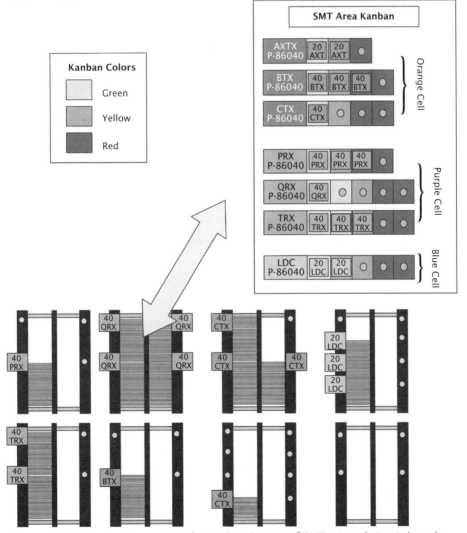

Figure 11.3. The kanban system for replenishment of SMT printed circuit boards.

The number of pcbs to a panel needs to be considered when deciding the maximum stock holding of each panel type. Clearly, the more pcbs a certain type of panel contains, the fewer the number of panels that will have to be held for a given rate of consumption. In order for the kanban to work well, somewhere between 4 and 12 kanban tickets are needed for each different type of pcb. Just one or two tickets won't allow the traffic-light visual-priority system to work; but too many tickets will increase the effort in managing the kanban. To achieve the right balance, kanban cards can be made to represent 40 panels of high-volume pcb types, compared to only 20 panels for low-volume pcb types. A few basic calculations combined with common sense is all that is necessary to design a kanban ticket system that enables a sensible number of both kanban tickets and pcb WIP to coexist.

The kanban board can be built on a sheet of MDF coated with white melamine. The kanban design can either be painted on or made up using colored paper (laminated for durability) to create the green, yellow, and red kanban squares. The best method for attaching the kanban tickets is to use Velcro patches. If tickets are absent from the board, it is because they are stuck to the appropriately filled lab rack. *Absent tickets thus represent quantities of WIP that are available for use.* A glance at the kanban board represents a rough-cut WIP count as well as indicating the current replenishment priorities. Different families of pcbs that are destined for use in different cells can be given individually colored tickets to aid identification.

Tickets that are missing from the board are located on lab racks. As the racks are emptied of pcb panels by the assembly cells, the appropriate tickets are returned to the correct section of the kanban board, always filling the spaces from left to right.

Panels of SMT built pcbs are one of the most expensive items of inventory on the shop floor. A kanban ticket system such as this allows small but practical quantities of material to be held, allowing downstream assembly cells to respond flexibly to demand for product. As the downstream operations use up the pcbs, they replace the tickets onto the kanban board. As the SMT section builds more panels, they refill the lab racks, and the tickets are taken back off the board one by one and then fixed in the correct manner to the side of the racks as they refill them.

The system quickly and dynamically feeds back information to the SMT line as to how the replenishment priorities are changing. The assemblies that are most regularly consumed get replenished most frequently; those that are slow moving get replenished only occasionally.

SMT production run lengths are limited by the availability of kanban tickets; usually the run stops short of stripping all the available tickets off the board because invariably other types of pcb have crept into the red in the mean time, indicating that they are a more urgent build priority. This kanban system helps the SMT team to plan what is the correct priority setup to prepare for next, thus avoiding frustrations experienced when the decisions on what to run are either not forthcoming from the supervisory team or, in their absence, are hastily made educated guesses made by people out of touch with what is going on.

Replenishment of Molded Plastic Components

In a press shop or injection molding area, the quantity and volume of parts being produced will be considerable, even after SMED initiatives have allowed the batch sizes to be reduced. How can such a production department be planned without the use of a central stores facility, several indirect storemen, and the intervention of a production planner?

The practice of counting work into a store and then booking it out to the assembly departments as (and when) needed is not adding value. Replacing this situation with something better can appear daunting because the logistical problems involved seem so large.

Here is an example of one way it can be achieved. To set the scene, in preparation for a factory move, it is decided that the injection-molding operation will have to be restructured because there will not be sufficient space to have a central storeroom within the future factory building. At the old site, the injection-molding department was always causing the downstream assembly departments to run out of components. The planning was, in fact, so poor that it was often the case that jobs that had just been put up had to be taken down immediately for a red-hot "screamer" requirement that had only just been discovered. The mold-shop planning sheet as produced by the Production Planner did not convey much information, and it certainly had no visual impact, merely being a list of part numbers written against numbers representing the different mold machines. It didn't really matter that the duration for all of these molding jobs was left unspecified, because the plan would change each day as new red-hot urgencies were discovered. Everyone, especially the mold-shop operators and setters, were very frustrated with the whole process.

Instead of this perhaps familiar scenario continuing day-in and day-out, a new system was needed that would allow not only the mold shop workers but, in fact, anyone to see the following.

- What jobs are currently running?

- What will be the next jobs to go up?

- When will the changeovers be made?

- How long will the jobs be running?

- Which machines have spare capacity?

What was needed was a large planning board in the department, where the week's work being planned for each of the six molding machines could be displayed. Tickets for each individual job would be required, showing as much useful information as possible, such as what containers to use, storage locations, and the mold machine program numbers. A multiple-ticket kanban system would be too complicated for this, but a single-ticket kanban would realistically work. The first step in creating this new system was to gather all the information on every molding job that existed, and to arrange it on the first page of a computer spreadsheet. On the second page of the same spreadsheet, the kanban tickets were designed, with different sections holding the various items of data; information from the first page is transferred to each section on the kanban tickets shown on the second page. In this way, when the data gets updated, new tickets can be issued without too much difficulty.

Despite the quantity of information to be displayed, the size of the tickets has to be limited so that the kanban-planning board will not have to become too large in size. The kanban board that was built was sectioned off into separate horizontal strips for each machine's workload, and separate vertical strips for each shift across the whole of the week (see **Figure 11.4**). Nails were hammered into the board, onto which the kanban tickets would be hung. The compromise on space meant that there could only be four nail "time periods" per shift provided, meaning that each nail would represent two hours of run time.

Kanban tickets fixed to the board indicate which machines are running which jobs. The gap between adjacent tickets for a given mold machine is decided by the run time stated on the left-most ticket. Where only two shifts (double-days) are running, the darker bands representing night shifts are skipped and ignored. Where it is possible for a job to be run on two or even three different molding machines, the decision of what machine to use is given to the leading hand of the department. The decision would be based on the particular mix of work for the coming week, the resulting machine capacity, and the experience of knowing which jobs run best on which machines.

The kanban tickets suspended horizontally on the board using bulldog clips indicate the jobs that are currently running. The current moment is indicated by a large pink elastic band stretched vertically across the board. This helps to show how close to the next setup each machine is or, conversely, how long the current jobs have been running.

It was found that it was best to have just one independent person responsible for the management of the planning board. If several people are allowed to move tickets around, the situation soon loses its objectiveness, as tickets are moved according to which customer cell screams the loudest, and mold setters can abuse the system to avoid performing setups during their own shift.

Molding Component Kanban Tickets

The leading hand of any downstream assembly section will always be very keen to ensure that his/her operators do not run out of components. It is

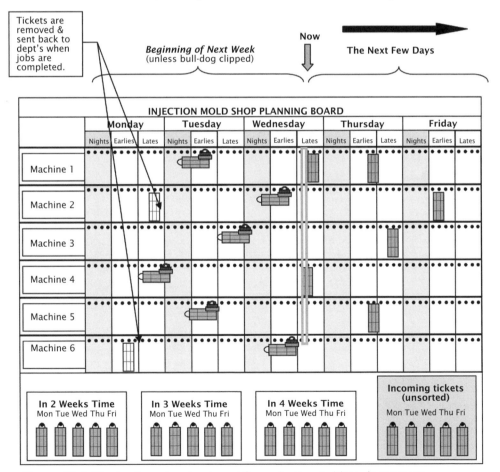

Figure 11.4. The kanban planning board for a plastics molding department.

therefore a good idea to make these leading hands responsible for triggering the replenishment of any of their own plastic moldings.

In this example, each assembly area leading hand has a check sheet showing all of the molded components that are used in their own area (see **Figure 11.5**). Beside each listed part there is a "trigger" point: i.e., if the moldings fall below this quantity, then the relevant kanban ticket needs to be sent back to the mold shop. When the tickets are taken over to the mold shop planning board, they are added to the section of the board for "incoming tickets" to be later sorted into priority by the mold shop leading hand.

Every job must utilize two (or more) *full* tubs/boxes. By knowing how many components fill a box of a given size, one avoids the need to physically count the individual parts themselves. In this example, it is necessary for some smaller components to have to wait for up to 4 weeks to be molded because, even with the smallest containers, two tubs might still contain 10 weeks worth at a normal consumption rate of components. The trigger for such parts is similar to a two-bin system: use up one of the two tubs and the ticket is released. At the opposite end of the scale, with some of the larger moldings where it is only possible to get 24 components in even the largest of the available boxes, four pallets worth of components produced in a single batch might be necessary; i.e., four pallets, each holding 15 large boxes each containing 24 moldings = 1440 units. It is expected that this quantity will be enough for only 2 $^{1}/_{2}$ weeks. In this instance, the trigger point may need to be at 55 of the possible 60 full boxes, so that "in two weeks time" the assembly area does not run out.

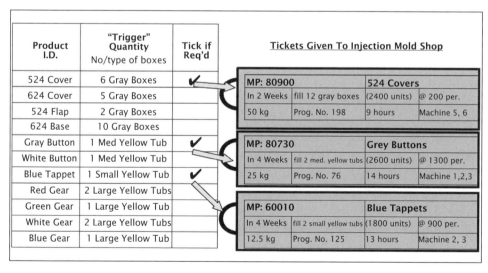

Figure 11.5. Assembly cells have check sheets to prompt the return of tickets to the molding department.

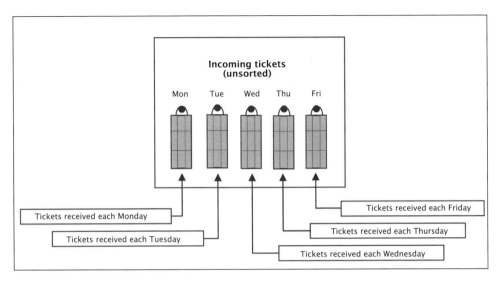

Figure 11.6. Incoming tickets are placed on a holding board by the mold shop leading hand.

When the trigger points are hit, each assembly area's leading hand makes a daily trip to the molding department to drop off the relevant kanban tickets. They are then collected and stored each day on the planning board as shown in **Figure 11.6**.

In this way, even though the planning board is geared up to work in weekly snapshots, during any given week the board can take into account at which point in the week the tickets came back from the assembly areas. This helps ensure the jobs get loaded onto the board in the correct order of priority, which should minimize the risk of a stock-out.

Updating the Week's Plan

Once the board has been running for several weeks, there will be a degree of planning stability, tickets will have been loaded onto the board in all the sections, and there will be appropriate levels of WIP on the shop floor for each assembly area.

At the end of the week, the mold shop leading hand takes the tickets that have been sitting in the "In 2 Weeks Time" section and, starting with "Monday," the tickets get loaded onto the planning board, hung on the next free nail after considering how long the prior job will run. Next, the Tuesday tickets go up, etc. Once all of the "In 2 Weeks Time" tickets are up, it is possible to see that some machines might be tight for capacity and so some tickets may get shuffled onto other machines that are less utilized. If that is not enough to resolve any conflicts, some of the tickets might have to be spaced closer together than originally planned. If there still is not enough capacity, the leading hand knows that overtime or three-shift working may now be necessary. If there is overcapacity and the tickets don't fill all the time available, then some machines are allowed to stop for several hours, providing a good opportunity to perform planned maintenance.

If the overcapacity is ongoing, it may indicate the need to reduce the number of shifts. Finer adjustments can be had by running one or more days of the week with just a single morning shift, and transferring the afternoon workers into other parts of the shop floor to attend to some other worthwhile work priority. Once the "In 2 Weeks Time" section has been emptied, the tickets can be shuffled forward from the third and fourth weeks, keeping them in the same Monday to Friday order (see **Figure 11.7**).

Sorting Incoming Tickets

Only now can the mold shop leading hand take the tickets that have been

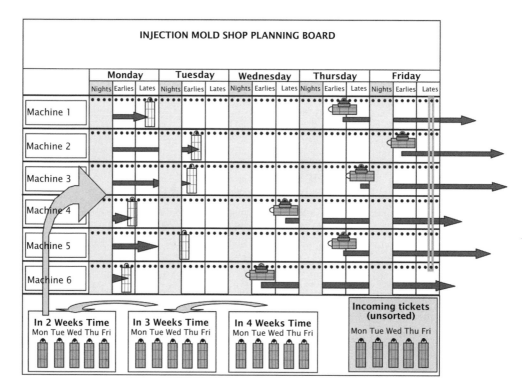

Figure 11.7. All tickets are shuffled forward into their next position at the end of each week.

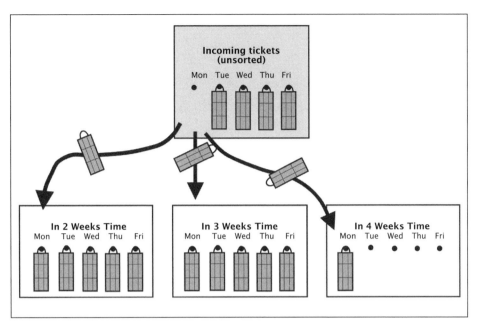

Figure 11.8. Holding board tickets are now organized into the appropriate waiting positions.

accumulating in the "Incoming Tickets (unsorted)" section and put them into the next stage on the board, as shown in **Figure 11.8**. This starts to prioritize the tickets into which jobs will be put up "in 2 weeks time" and which are less of a priority and will be put up in 3–4 weeks time. This distinction is dependant on whether the ticket states replenish "in 4 weeks time" (likely to be a small, short-cycle/multicavity part) or "in 2 weeks time" (probably a large component with a single molding cavity and a long molding cycle).

The tickets that came in at the very start of the week (i.e., Monday) will get moved to the Monday section of either the 2, 3, or 4 weeks time card storage sections. The tickets that came in on Tuesday get separated out into the 3 possible Tuesdays of the coming weeks, and so on, until all the tickets have been allocated and the "Incoming Tickets" section has been emptied.

Once the molded components are delivered to the lineside storage area, the relevant ticket also gets returned. It is a good idea for the leading hand of each assembly area to have a ticket storage board beside their desk. This provides a set location to which the kanban tickets can be returned to and retrieved from, without wasting time searching for them or risking losing any.

Expediting

Should there be a "screamer" (such occasions will now be much rarer), the required job ticket will almost certainly already be on the kanban planning board. The mold shop leading hand can now make an informed decision about what to do because the possible consequences of such actions are now far more visible.

Replenishing Raw Materials

The planning system above will need the rest of the supply chain to be as dynamic as it is. Therefore, empower the leading hand to order his/her own materials within a controlled framework such as faxbans (see Chapter 23, "Support for Lean Manufacturing").

Chapter 12

Steps in Designing a Lean Cell

All too often when an organization makes a change, an inadequate amount of planning occurs, which at the same time takes up a disproportionately large amount of time. The causes can be varied, but usually there are three common factors contributing to the problem: people inherently resist change; a general assumption that consensus is required and must be sought no matter how much time is wasted; and that too much time is spent concentrating on short-term problems and day-to-day fire-fighting activities.

Traditional Change Effort			Optimal Change Effort	
Effort	**Time**		**Effort**	**Time**
5%	6 Months	— PLAN —	30%	2–4 Weeks
95%	3 Weeks	— DO —	60%	2–5 Days
0%	N/A	— REVIEW —	10%	1/4–1/2 Day

Creating a lean cell will deliver many benefits to the organization—it is worth planning it correctly and also doing it quickly (i.e., a "blitz" approach). When done properly, planning can reduce implementation time because many mistakes and unforeseen problems can be avoided. If the lean disciples planning the cell are allowed to focus on their goal, and are wise to the fact that an unanimous consensus is unnecessary, then the planning stage can be made both effective and short.

When embarking on a long car journey to an unknown part of the country, it may be possible to get to the destination just by having the confidence in your own sense of direction and reading the road signs along the way. This approach may get you there, but it almost certainly won't be by the most direct route, in the shortest possible time, or at the lowest cost. A better approach would be to spend time prior to your departure examining a map, planning the best route, and making a few notes on milestones to be passed during the course of the journey. This will invariably result in a quicker and less stressful trip. Likewise, when creating a new lean cell, omitting some aspects of the planning stage before moving the equipment and benches can certainly cause time, money, and credibility to be lost. Putting a greater emphasis on planning change properly is not the same as being indecisive and delaying taking the first step.

It is also common to see changes being made without a followup to determine whether or not the change was a success. Mistakes will always be made, but this can be a good thing; without mistakes it is very hard to learn what works and what doesn't. Omitting the review step in the change process prevents the team from learning and developing itself—without continuous learning, the members of the implementation team will not gain confidence in themselves, and they will continue to feel dependent on the support of outside consultants. The review stage also helps to define what progress has been made, thereby keeping the team motivated and focused.

The reason that WIP builds up is because consecutive production operations have different work rates, e.g., where a faster job builds up work behind a slower one. Many of these buildups can be eliminated. In order to assure that work flows smoothly and continuously, jobs need to be rebalanced so that the different operations (combined) are performed at as close to the same rate as possible.

Traditionally, every individual job would be required to work as fast as possible to maximize the productivity performance of the shop floor. However, the truth is that *slowing down* the fastest operations will improve a cell's aggregate performance. This would be a contemptible and illogical suggestion if it meant operators should be slowing down. Instead, what is actually meant makes a great deal of sense: by shifting elements of work normally done as part of a slow neighboring operation, and making it part of a faster job, the consecutive cycle times can be brought into a better state of balance. Where this is not practical, rules can be put in place so that the fastest operations are only run for quite short bursts, and operators will then move onto other tasks that are more immediately required. The operators will have to demonstrate a greater degree of flexibility and multiskilling across all the jobs in the cell. Doing both of these things greatly improves the overall process, because WIP buildups are dramatically reduced, allowing the lead time of the entire process to shrink to a small fraction of what it once was, resulting in leanness.

Designing the new lean production process has five distinct steps.
1. Identify where large areas of continuous work flow can be achieved.
2. Decide what the takt time is for the products in question.

3. Collate a detailed list of operation times throughout that area for the product.
4. Start the process of balancing the new "continuous flow cell."
5. Plan how to connect the continuous flow cell with its upstream/downstream neighboring processes (probably kanban, perhaps make-to-order).

Identifying Where Continuous Work Flow is Achievable

Any series of successive operations working the same shift pattern as each other and downstream of any "batch building" processes, such as stamping or molding, can usually be remodelled to achieve continuous work flow. This makes assembly, testing, and packing highly suitable for lean improvements, and such areas normally represent significant proportions of the factory.

Types of Continuous Work Flow

One-piece flow. This is the ultimate form of lean production, but unfortunately it cannot be applied to every situation. Operators are only allowed to work on one workpiece at a time, and no material queues between successive operations are allowed. This requires excellent work rate balancing of consecutive operations.

Multipiece flow. This is the next-best compromise that can be applied to most situations. Small, single figure numbers of subassemblies are allowed to build up between successive operations. When an operator has built up the limited amount of WIP, or runs out of workpieces to process, he/she has to move to an unmanned operation somewhere else in the cell downstream or upstream in order to keep the work flowing. In this way, out-of-balance situations can be overcome without a loss in output efficiency, but the massive reductions in lead time and waste are still realized.

One word of caution before continuing: continuous work flow is best done in a cell containing just a small group of people working effectively as a team. One to three people can balance work between themselves fairly easily so that the work flows one piece at a time without anyone having to wait for the next unit to come along. However, a team of eight people, although able to be an effective team, will find efficient one-piece flow unrealistic because there are now too many opportunities for the work flow to become disrupted. Instead, for a cell that requires this many people, there are two options.

1. The team operates using multipiece flow, where single-figure quantities

of WIP are allowed to accumulate and operators keep moving to different parts of the cell to keep the work flowing. This method works well in lean cell design for any number of operators between one and ten.

2. Seven or eight operators can be linked together to still allow fast moving work flow by using a hybrid between one-piece flow and multipiece flow. If the cell is designed with several spare workstations built into it—for example, twelve positions to be manned by eight people—the team can be broken down into twos and threes: i.e., a front section, a middle section, and an end section with small two-bin systems connecting them. A three man team carrying out one-piece flow reduces to two, or increases from two to three people, depending on the degree to which work has built up between them.

A cell with *more* than eight people will simply be too large to communicate and interact properly; and such a team will no longer work very effectively. For example, even an 11-man football squad has to be organized into two teams—the forwards and the backs. If an area of continuous-flow exceeds 6–8 people, then, like a football team, it should be split into two or more separate cells connected by a two-bin or a kanban system.

Calculating Takt Time

Before designing a new cell, the first thing that needs to be done is to determine what the cell's *maximum output rate* will need to be. Without knowing this, the cell might be designed too small, not having enough capacity to cope with periods of peak demand. Conversely, the cell might be designed too large, wasting space, wasting equipment, and causing unnecessary people and material movements.

Takt time is the rate at which the cell needs to produce finished units; it can be described as the drumbeat or rhythm of the cell. The cell's takt time has to be based upon the maximum rate of demand. If a kanban facility of buffer stock is planned to exist after the cell, the takt time can be the average daily demand in the *peak* month.

$$\textbf{Takt time} = \frac{\text{Available work time per day}}{\text{Maximum customer sales demand per day}}$$

Before calculating the takt time, it is worth considering the following.
1. Can the spikes in customer demand that determine the maximum daily rate be smoothed by a) having the sales staff encourage customers toward smaller but more frequent deliveries, and/or b) the shop

floor being prepared to hold kanban stocks of product waiting to be customized?

2. In the longer term, what changes in sales demand are expected for the product? If demand is likely to increase significantly, extra capacity will need to be planned into the new cell, possibly by adding more workstations.

Example

The first lean cell that our fictitious factory will be designing is for the production of fire alarm control panels called the "Sentinel" range. After reviewing historical sales data and consulting with the sales manager about opportunities for order smoothing or for holding kanban stocks, it becomes possible to identify a realistic maximum number of units needing to be produced on any one day.

In this example, although the *average* demand for Sentinels seems to be 280 per day when the peaks in demand are considered, the *maximum* demand that the cell will need to produce will be more like 374 units per day. The product is to be assembled using a team of people working an eight-hour day.

Sentinel's **Takt Time =**

$$\frac{8 \text{ hr} \times 60 \text{ min/hr} \times 60 \text{ sec/min}}{374 \text{ units}} = \frac{28{,}800 \text{ sec}}{374 \text{ units}} = 77 \text{ sec}$$

This means that the cell needs to be capable of producing one unit every 77 seconds. If the flow of work can be kept as continuous as possible, it can literally be visualized as one finished unit appearing from the cell every 1¼ minutes.

The Value Stream Mapping Technique

Value stream mapping is a comprehensive analytical tool that is frequently used by consultants and is also useful to lean disciples for identifying areas across the entire production process where lean improvements can be made. It is usual to include the suppliers and customers in the map, as well as communication methods. This allows for a holistic analysis of all the facts and all the opportunities for maximizing lean benefits. To demonstrate the changes and improvements intended, a before-and-after value stream map is drawn. The basic symbols and notation within a value stream map are shown in Figures 12.1 and 12.2.

Describing an Operation

Each separate operation may be shown as a text box (**Figure 12.1a**). Below the title section, a full account of all the important operational details that are relevant is provided, including facts about changeover times, machine reliability, and (if appropriate) reject rates/yield.

Describing WIP Inventory and Work Flow

A triangle labeled "I" for inventory is used to describe the presence of a WIP queue. An arrow underneath describes the direction that the work is flowing (**Figure 12.1b**). Directly under the "I" triangle is a fair estimate of the typical/average WIP quantity to be found at that point in the process.

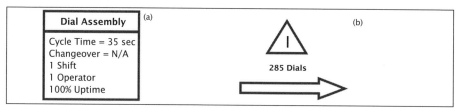

Figure 12.1. The primary symbols used in the value stream map are the data box (a), and the WIP/inventory tag (b).

Describing the Value-Add and Nonvalue-Add Periods

Below each separate operation's text box, and the gap between operations described by the inventory triangle and flow arrow, is a castellated line (**Figure 12.2**). The upper parts of this line denote the waiting times of inventory sitting in queues. The lower parts denote the value-adding times of each operation. At the end of the line (usually shown flowing left to right) are two more text boxes, showing the cumulative waiting time and the value-add time. The waiting time is usually so large that it approximates the lead time. An example of the usefullness of completing the value stream mapping technique is shown in **Figure 12.3**. Please note that this example is unrelated to the "Sentinel" which we will soon continue to discuss.

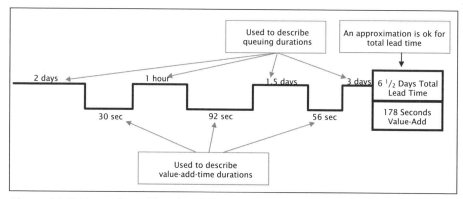

Figure 12.2. How value-add and nonvalue-add time is represented in the map.

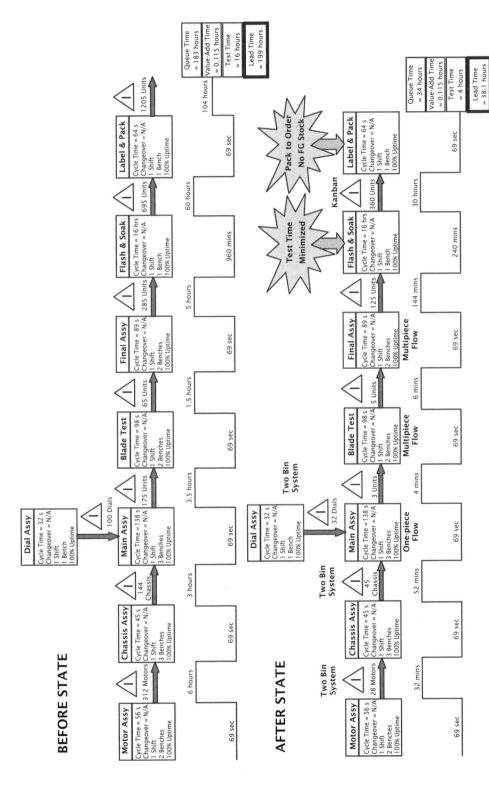

Figure 12.3. The before and after value stream mapping technique.

Although mapping the entire process may highlight several different areas that can be improved, the main objective will be to find areas where continuous flow can be created by changing the area to become a lean cell. To do this, it is practical to apply certain limitations using common sense and good judgment. Look for a point in the production system where the processes with significant tool-changeover issues and shift-working sections give way to areas on day shift, performing tasks such as assembly, testing, and packing.

Gathering Operational Times for Work Balancing Purposes

A competent production-orientated lean disciple, who has been with the company for over two years, should have little problem producing the information on manufacturing a product family such as the Sentinel range for use in a value stream map. Key data are the *operational times*—or the machine cycle times at each value-adding part of the process—and any issues of changeover times, equipment reliability (% uptime), and the shift/overtime patterns. It is best not to rely on time-study data that might be years old and riddled with inaccuracies. Instead, go out on the shop floor with a stopwatch, a pencil, and some post-it notes, and gather the information first hand, remembering to take an average time calculated over 5–10 workpieces. It is a good idea to involve one or two operators who actually build the product in recording and verifying these operational times.

Remember that using post-it notes was also recommended during SMED workshops, and the reason for doing so this time is the same. They provide a lot of flexibility, allowing extra items to be added, or unnecessary ones (nonvalue-add operations) to be removed with less difficulty than if working on one large sheet of paper. Examples can be seen in **Figure 12.4**.

It is not good enough just to document the half dozen traditional operations that describe several actions that had been grouped together for convenience. Every value-adding activity that can be done separately from any other value-adding activity must be described individually. We aren't particularly interested in the nonvalue-add operations (fetching materials, looking for tools, moving trays of work) because the objective is to try to design a process where the work flows, where double-handling is largely avoided, and where the materials are close at hand. When everyone is confident that none of the activities can be broken down into any smaller constituent parts, that each activity has a correct time assigned to it, and that the correct work sequence has been documented, the work balancing stage can begin.

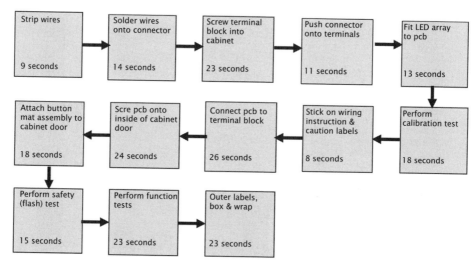

Figure 12.4. Post-it notes are ideal for making an initial breakdown of separate operations.

Work Balancing the New Lean Cell

Sentinel control panels are currently assembled and packed using six separate benches—one for each of the main operations that the lean team has now realized can be broken down further into even smaller blocks of work. This realization will make the job of rearranging the work into new balanced groupings much easier.

			Broken-down times (see Figure 12.4)
Op1	27 sec.	Wiring harness build	9 s and 18 s
Op2	34 sec.	Wiring box assembly	23 s and 11 s
Op3	55 sec.	Front panel build	13 s, 18 s, and 24 s
Op4	34 sec.	Main assembly	26 s and 8 s
Op5	56 sec.	Set operational limits and safety test	18 s, 15 s, and 23 s
Op6	23 sec.	Label, pack, and wrap	23 s

Labor Content = **229 sec.**   Takt Time = **77 sec.**

Operators in Cell = 229 ÷ 77 = 2.97 (**3 people**)

The redesigned cell needs to be grouped into *three blocks of work* (one for each of the three operators that are needed), as can also be seen in **Figure 12.5,** with each being as equal to each other and as close to the takt time as possible. Ideally, just three benches can be used, but if it is more realistic, 4, 5, or even all of the previously required 6 benches can be used to contain all the equipment and materials. Then, the cell can be laid out to suit. But remember, the fewer the benches, the closer the operators can be to each other and the easier it will be to keep the work flowing.

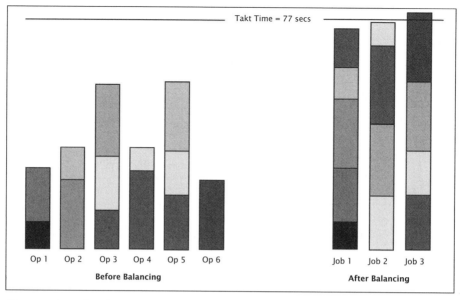

Figure 12.5. Closely balancing operations so they equal the takt time will smooth work flow.

Balancing Suggestions

The calculation just performed indicated that there should be 2.97 operators. What if it hadn't been so close to a whole number?

2.1–2.3   Run the cell with just two people, because the calculation was based on the maximum demand. If a small amount of safety stock is held, two individuals are likely to keep up with average demand, and the safety stock will help them to cope with any spikes in demand. They can then replenish stock to the agreed level on quieter days.

2.4–2.6   Can any other minor value-adding jobs be transferred into the cell from somewhere else? A small extra workload would achieve a better balancing; for example, the crimping of terminals onto wires or perhaps a small riveting operation. A few jobs like these would get the manning requirement closer to 2.9 and might be what's needed for getting an even closer balance between the operators.

2.7–2.9   This is ideal. Run the cell with 3 people in a balanced manner with excellent work flow to produce the quantity of product required, then stop the cell entirely when the order requirement has been fulfilled. Three operators means that there is sufficient capacity to allow some time for such things as cell meetings, material replenishment, and housekeeping at points throughout the day or week.

Running the New Lean Cell

The three new balanced jobs are 74, 76, and 79 seconds in duration, respectively. Balancing perfectly has not been possible, but the action of splitting the original operations down into very small elements helps achieve an acceptable balance nevertheless. Just because the three new job groups are balanced, it doesn't mean that they will remain so if the three operators are left to their own devices. Once the new cell layout has been put in place, the next hurdle to be tackled will be to break any remnants of old shop floor culture that might spoil the smooth and efficient flow of work.

- Some operator initiative should be encouraged to keep the line in balance by trimming itself (moving very small value-add activities from one operator to another). However, don't allow a dominant individual to unfairly offload work onto the other two. If the team has to carry one individual, it will effectively slow the entire process down.

- One operator stopping at any time, whether to talk, go to the toilet, or because he/she has run out of a part, will cause the other two to stop also. Left unchecked, the team may be quite satisfied to sit there and "rest" every time that this happens. Again, this will result in a shortfall in the day's expected output.

Inevitably, some people are faster or more dexterous than others; it is preferable that the team members be of similar ability to help them stay in balance. Operators need to be asked to take toilet visits only at appropriate times. If one does have to stop for a short time, then the other two should use it as an opportunity to refill *everyone's* part bins, not just their own. If one person is stopped for a moderate amount of time (e.g., a tool breaks), all three should do any rework that they can, and then the team leader should reallocate them all to different jobs elsewhere. The new continuous flow cell will need to be observed and coached by a supervisor or a lean disciple until it proves that it knows how to operate, knows what is expected of it, and performs at a consistently high standard.

To Incorporate Packing or Not?

When designing a lean cell, it is very important to incorporate product testing within the cell whenever possible. Doing this will eliminate the possibility of the cell producing an excessive number of rejects before the problem is discovered. Leaving final testing out of the cell opens up the risk of finding large quantities of failures so late in the day that nothing constructive can be done about it.

Whether or not to incorporate packing into a lean cell depends on a single consideration. You should *not* include it if the product gets packaged differently for different customers, and you are (as yet) unable to build today what is going to be shipped today/tomorrow. In this situation, you will need to hold some kanban stocks of built product that can then be packed-to-order as a last minute customization function. However, if each product gets packed in the same carton every time, then incorporate this work into the cell. This will really reduce the overall lead time and may allow the cell to be even better balanced.

Logistical Cell Design Considerations and Options

Depending what the takt time calculations recommend, in terms of the number of operators required and the practical problems of creating cells that operate along lean principles, there are several possibilities that can be encountered.

A key consideration is how much equipment and material exists. If it amounts to very little, then it might be possible to fit it all on one bench. If this is the case, one cannot improve on a one-man cell, but the combinations of benches and operators required beyond this leads to a variety of cell design options.

All equipment and parts can be stored on *one bench.*

- One operator required: Design a single-operator cell.
- Two operators required: Choose between two one-man cells or a two-person, two bench one-piece-flow cell.
- Three operators required: Either have three one-man cells or a 3-person, 2–3 bench one-piece flow cell.

Two benches are necessary to contain all the equipment/parts.

- One operator required: Design a single one-man cell, with two benches at 90 degrees.
- Two operators required: Design a two-person cell with two workstations and one-piece flow.
- Three operators required: Use the minimum number of benches to fit three people, and have one-piece flow.

Three benches are necessary to contain all the equipment/parts.

- One operator required: Design a single one-man cell, with three benches in a U shape. The more tools that are needed to be handled by an individual, the better it is to use multipiece flow rather than one-piece flow.

- Two operators required: Design a cell with three benches, with two mobile operators, and *multi*piece flow.

- Three operators required: Have one three-person one-piece-flow cell.

- Four operators required: Use four benches, arranged as two separate two-man one-piece-flow cells with a two-bin replenishment link between them.

Single-Person One-Piece Flow Cells

Creating cells that consist of just one person is often the ideal way of easily achieving one-piece flow. A single-person cell is often possible if there is only a small number of both parts and tools needed to make the product. One bench is ideal, and two or more benches should only be used when only one cell is required, or when the process is machinery intensive and necessitates it. Single-person assembly cells are frequently possible when the process time is quite short. If the total build time is greater than the takt time, then you simply need to ensure you have duplicated or triplicated single-person cells available.

Why is the single-person cell scenario so ideal?

- One person gets full satisfaction in knowing he/she has built the entire product.

- The operator gets to take on full responsibility for the quality and output rate—there's nobody else to blame or hide behind.

- Work balancing occurs naturally.

- One-piece flow (build one, then test it, build one, then test it) is a total reality.

- There is no opportunity for the operator to be forced to wait for a slower colleague.

An Example of Takt Calculation Where One-Person Cells Are Possible

This example product is a programmable security switch. Because it is of a fairly small size, and it doesn't comprise of very many components (given that the pcb it uses is already assembled), relatively little bench space is required. The build sequence is:

Op1	14 sec.	Put 2 screws and 2 nuts into base molding
Op2	14 sec.	Swage threads of screws using arbor press
Op3	38 sec.	Fit display LCD to pcb
Op4	13 sec.	Solder blob links on pcb

Op5   6 sec.   Screw pcb onto base molding
Op6   3 sec.   Fit slider switch molding
Op7   10 sec.   Fit buttons and button mats into cover molding
Op8   7 sec.   Assemble base face down into cover and screw together
Op9   8 sec.   Stick on capacity, warranty, and wiring labels
Op10   36 sec.   Fit to testing unit, go through test cycle
Op11   4 sec.   Remove from tester, stamp, and place in tray.

Demand for this group of products is 6000/month, 300/day. Peak demand is 380/day.

$$\text{Takt} = 28{,}800 \div 380 = 76 \text{ seconds}$$

$$\text{Total work content} = 153 \text{ seconds}$$

The number of operators required = $153 \div 76 = 2.01$; two operator stations are required.

When to Pick Multipiece-Flow Over One-Piece Flow

In many instances, one-piece flow is not feasible. A common reason for this is that the operations that need to be included in a cell cannot be balanced close enough to use one-piece flow effectively. The alternative is to allow for the natural flexibility of the operators, asking them to keep moving around the cell so that work buildups can be minimized.

Another reason for settling for multipiece-flow is that the work has to go through a piece of machinery where it needs to be processed in small transfer batches (a test operation that needs to be filled with 5 units each time). Another example of this might be where small pcbs may have been combined together into a matrix of six to a sheet. In this situation, operators will also find it easier to perform plated-through-hole build, flow soldering and hand soldering operations, while the pcbs remain connected as a matrix. The point at which they do need to be separated is immediately prior to testing on the automatic testing equipment (ATE).

A final example where multipiece-flow would be chosen would be when three operators are working in a cell that requires 6–7 benches/machines, and all the operation times at each workstation are relatively short. In this case, they would find themselves moving around the cell too frequently unless some small transfer batches were allowed. To insist on one-piece flow would waste too much operator motion time.

Even in these compromised situations, a good degree of continuous flow is still possible, allowing for greatly shortened lead times to be achieved.

Multipiece-Flow Cells

In the following example, a company specializing in manufacturing security alarms and fire alarms is resolved to moving away from large transfer batches to a lean continuous flow methodology in its printed circuit board production area.

Its range of industrial fire alarms use power-supply pcbs of which there are eight subtly different variants, all the same size, and all to be made in the same cell. This pcb cell will be comprised of build (conventional components into plated through-holes), inspection (inspect, hand solder wires to the board, remove peelable solder-resist masking), and test operations.

It is becoming apparent that one-piece flow doesn't seem to be achievable in this instance for two significant reasons. The first reason is that each sheet of power supply pcbs is made of a matrix of four individual boards that remain joined together until the pcbs are almost completed. The second reason is the fact that the area has a shared process—a flow solder machine. The power supply cell won't be able to monopolize this machine because it must also process the work from the four other pcb build sections. The flow solder machine has a width-adjustable caterpillar conveyor, and the machine can only solder one width of pcb at any one time. Although the width is readily adjustable, each of the five different families of pcb sheets (the power supply pcb is just one of these families) is of different width. It is therefore appropriate to run at least 10–12 sheets of one type through the $2\frac{1}{2}$-meter-long conveyor before another small batch of a different sheet width is processed.

The area (soon to be a lean cell) making these power supply boards needs to build 9,600 pcbs each month for the downstream assembly of the fire alarm systems. The customer demand profile is very uniform, and because there are no large spikes, the build number per day can be considered as an average 480 units. The cell will normally run just a single eight-hour day.

$$\text{Takt time} = \frac{8 \times 60 \times 60}{480} = 60 \text{ seconds}$$

Op1   40 sec.   Conventional component plated through-hole build
Op2   15 sec.   Flow solder (not included in cell)
Op3   28 sec.   Inspect, trim, breakout
Op4   55 sec.   ATE testing—in circuit and functional tests
Op5   35 sec.   Transformer strapping (tie wrap), then solder on three
                connection leads
Op6   13 sec.   Rework as necessary for ATE failures (average time per
                board)
Total = 171 seconds of work per pcb

Number of operators required = 171 ÷ 60 = 2.85. It is therefore decided that three people are typically required but the cell will also need to be able to run effectively with two people from time to time.

Rules for Operating this Multipiece-Flow Pcb Cell

Multipiece-flow is a very good compromise to achieving continuous flow, but unless there are strict rules to limit any excessive buildup of WIP, operators will almost certainly start batching up work excessively and reverting to nonlean production. One form of build-up limitation is to allow only a limited number of *small* containers to exist within the cell. Another is simply to state that once one small container is full, the operator must leave that operation and move to clear a work buildup elsewhere. In the same manner, as soon as an operator finds himself or herself starved of work, he/she must move to an empty bench at the start of the cell to get more work being built.

In the example shown in **Figure 12.6**, only two "half" lab racks are allowed in the cell, into which up to 12 sheets (each a matrix of 4 individual pcbs) of Op1 work are placed before the rack is taken away for soldering. Flow soldered sheets are then returned to the cell on small antistatic slotted "toast-stands." Again, only two full trays were allowed, each holding 12 sheets.

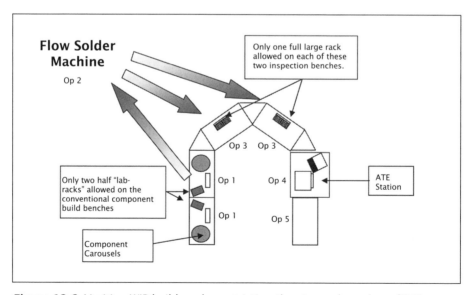

Figure 12.6. Limiting WIP buildups by restricting the size and number of WIP containers, together with good operator coaching can be very effective in keeping WIP low, and work flow moving fast.

With two or more operators, you can see that with six possible stations, there is always a vacant workstation for the operator to move to, thus keeping the work flowing. If the cell was designed to be as small as possible, as shown in **Figure 12.7**, with the minimum number of stations, then there are not enough spare stations for one of the three operators to move to when they've reached the transfer batch limit.

If the cell is designed like this, the operator's only option would be to break the rules and keep building (destroying leanness), or wait for the out-of-balance process to catch up, causing losses in productivity. So, a key factor in designing a multipiece-flow cell is to allow additional workstations to enable operators to move to the work. This is done at the expense of using more floor space than might otherwise be necessary if one-piece flow could have been utilized.

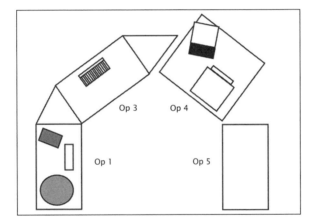

Figure 12.7. Reducing the number of benches to the bare minimum can result in reduced flexibility and productivity. Using the layout in this illustration, there is little opportunity for three operators to move around and follow the work.

Chapter 13

Before and After Measurement

There is much preparation work to do in the weeks prior to the "lean leap," when in a short, sharp blitz everything will get ripped up and reorganized. It may not seem important at the time when there is so much excitement in designing the new cells, but later on it will be regretted if the performance of the area was not measured *before* it was changed. Such data will allow comparisons to be made with the new lean methods, helping to justify the benefits of lean to any doubters. This information can also be used to congratulate the teams who were involved in making it happen. Being able to make such comparisons will give the organization's lean disciples an even greater depth of understanding of lean, making the next lean leap blitz an even bigger success.

Some comparisons can be made immediately, such as the before and after floor space used and the cumulative distance traveled by the components or walked by the operators. Other measures, such as quality (Right First Time %), productivity, housekeeping standards, and skill levels, will need a period of time before meaningful comparisons can be made.

CRITERIA TO MEASURE	Before Changes	After Changes
TOTAL SPACE	88.25 m²	35.5 m²
WALKING DISTANCE	124.2 m	23 m
PARTS TRAVEL DISTANCE	124.7 m	18 m
ACTUAL LEAD-TIME	10 hrs 38 min	5.8 min
WORK IN PROGRESS	$2,800	$350
PRODUCTIVITY:	74%	-
QUALITY (Right First Time %)	96%	- } TBA
HOUSEKEEPING SCORE:	32%	- } Later
SKILL LEVELS: (Average Skill-Points per Operator)	2	- }

SUMMARY OF WIP	Before Changes	After Changes
³/₄ Assembled Units	160	3
Dials	144	32
Motors	121	45
Chassis	312	32

An excellent addition to the table of before and after data will be some before and after photographs of the area. So remember to take photos before the area is changed!

Chapter 14

Rules on Visibility, Transparency, and Transferability

Visibility

Visibility for a workplace is a way of describing to how well everyone, including "outsiders," can see how it is organized, how it functions, and to what degree it displays key performance information about itself. When applied in a consistently high standard across the entire workplace, then the term "Visual Factory" can be used to describe it.

How Things are Organized

This speaks volumes about the standards to which the production team works, and is likely to be a reflection on the quality of its products. Done well in all aspects in conjunction with lean manufacturing, the cell can be described as world class. Some of the factors that are important are:

- how cell boundaries and entrances are defined,
- how work "footprints" are defined,
- the use of colors to define cell identity,
- how the cell stores and identifies its components,
- the presence of a kanban board and kanban tickets to show work priorities,
- the presence of component/subassembly identification display boards,
- how the workplace documents are stored/displayed, and their usefulness to operators,
- how tooling and equipment that is *not* currently in use is stored and arranged.

Cell Performance Measures and Charts

Supervisors, production planners, and quality inspectors are the people in control of traditional workplaces. Only limited information is given to the operators, and details on work performance are mostly summarized upwards to management in the shape of efficiency, reject, and scrap reports produced by the supervisors and quality inspectors.

This is a most unsatisfactory situation. A factory shop floor that is world class requires the production team to know how well they are performing each day. It should also allow any outsider/visitor to quickly see how well the cell is operating within a matter of moments. Clearly displaying key information on the team's performance within the cell can be used via cell meetings to encourage everyone to suggest improvements. These might be on topics such as how their work can be organized better, which pieces of equipment need to be made more reliable, and which component's lack of availability is causing the most problems. A suite of appropriate performance measures to display would be:

- **A Productivity Chart** for the team
- **A Skills Matrix** for all the cell's operators
- **Product "A" Quality:** 1) right-first-time %, 2) Pareto analysis, 3) reject cause breakdown
- **Product "B" Quality:** 1) right-first-time %, 2) Pareto analysis, 3) reject cause breakdown
- **Product "C" Quality:** 1) right-first-time %, 2) Pareto analysis, 3) reject cause breakdown
- **Housekeeping Standards**: Calculation table (with comments) and progress chart
- **Work Area Cleaning Rota**
- **Cell Meeting "Required Actions" list**.

Transparency

Transparency is the principle that "there is nothing hidden and nothing to hide." There should be nowhere to hide clutter, rejects, or scrap, and no need or wish to do so. When individuals hide such problems they are merely deceiving themselves. Why would anyone take such steps? Because they think they are going to get into trouble for making mistakes because there is a blame culture. While mistakes are being hidden, corrective actions can't even begin to be discussed, let alone implemented. For a modern organization to come up with kaizen improvements, it requires a culture of open communication, where managers and supervisors remain constructive and where people trust and respect each other.

Transferability

It is important that the presentation style in which things are done is consistent across the entire shop floor. The design of the kanban boards, the design of the performance charts, or even the colors used for cell floor markings, should all follow an agreed style. Doing so makes it easier for operators to move from cell to cell and assimilate themselves quickly into their new team. It makes it easier for visitors to the factory, or even workers from the office sections, to quickly feel familiar with the surroundings as they walk around the shop floor. It also makes good sense for the performance charts to be styled using the same formats and axis scales because it helps to make them easier to read and compare with one another.

Chapter 15

Housekeeping Standards

Why Most People Think Housekeeping is a Minor Issue

"Housekeeping! Housekeeping? That's not going to save the company any money!"

"We've got more important things to be sorting out than housekeeping!"

"The company has a good cleaning prior to each factory tour—that's good enough."

"A bit of tidying up won't increase profits or get the work out the door any faster!"

These rebuttals appear to have the voice of experience behind them and, in truth, when everyone is concentrating on short term issues such as rushing work through to the packing department, there appears to be little importance in such "minor" issues.

> *Waste reduction is the activity that gets the organization lean.*

It is *wasteful* to spend 5 minutes looking for the correct materials. It is *wasteful* spending 10 minutes looking for the correct jigs/fixtures or tooling. It is *wasteful* to find that the tools or materials you need are damaged and therefore can't be used because of the slapdash way in which they were stored.

The Benefits of High Standards of Housekeeping

Let us look at the benefits of good housekeeping standards in a little more detail.

Quicker Setups

During a SMED setup reduction workshop—when you are looking very closely to find out what's really going on in the setup/changeover for it to take so long—what do you find? People are looking for tools, looking for the right nuts and bolts, looking for the right materials, and looking for somewhere (a space, an empty shelf) to put the old materials that they've finished with. Faster setups are the first reason why a good standard of housekeeping is so important.

High Standards of Health and Safety

It can't be denied that there is a very strong connection between health and safety and standards of housekeeping—oil spills on the floor, clutter in the gangways, trailing electrical cables, benches overflowing with disorganization, boxes of work stacked precariously on top of one another. Health and safety (especially these days) is far too important to ignore.

Reject Reduction

I am sure you have experienced how bad housekeeping can be a chief cause of rejects when the wrong tools or components are picked up and used. A lot of mistake proofing can be achieved with better housekeeping standards.

More Effective Training

How much easier would it be for someone new to learn a job they had yet to perform if everything were arranged logically for them? Wouldn't it be easier if the components and equipment were clearly identified and clearly displayed? The answer is: yes, *it would be far easier*—easier for the trainee to learn, easier for the trainer to show. A byproduct of good housekeeping is that it makes for a more effective training environment and enables operators to become multiskilled far more quickly than would otherwise be possible.

Improved Productivity

If operators are more skilled, can perform setups in shorter times, make fewer mistakes, produce fewer rejects, and have fewer accidents, then the end result will be more output per direct payroll hour. Although cleaning takes time, cleaning a well-organized cell where clutter has already been eliminated is a far simpler and quicker task than trying to clean a disorganized work area.

Housekeeping Principles that Lean Disciples Must Believe In

Good housekeeping is based on high levels of *visibility, transparency,* and *transferability.*

Supervisors and leading hands are likely to be apathetic at first. Subconsciously they may perceive that if everyone else is able to find the required components/tools straight away, then their position might be undermined. Shop floor employees are likely to protest that they're too busy to stop and clean up. Instead they might suggest that someone else, such as a contract cleaner, perform such drudgery, leaving them to get on with "real" work.

This is a lame excuse for sloppiness! Don't accept the excuse that there's not enough time. There's always time for a chat, time to stop early for a break, time to have a joke and fill in a lottery ticket, etc. Do not expect anyone except you and your fellow lean disciples to be enthusiastic about housekeeping at first. The real goals and benefits of it will not be fully understood by the majority of people. For most, housekeeping means using a dustpan and brush at the end of each shift. In reality, only a very small proportion of good housekeeping is about being "clean."

The Initial Lean Leap Step Improvement in Housekeeping

When a lean cell is being created, two people in the lean team should be assigned to carry out a housekeeping "blitz" on the area. This will set the stage for becoming world class.

1. *Sort Out.* The first job is to define what items are always used, which are used only occasionally, and those that are never used.

   ✓ Mark those that are only *occasionally* used with *yellow* post-it notes.

   ✓ Mark things that are *never* used with *pink* post-it notes.

   Do this until everything—all the tools, jigs, machinery, shelves, and cupboards—have been sorted through.

2. *Clear Out.* Get rid of all the things with pink post-it notes. They are never used, or once were but are now obsolete. Cupboards should have their doors removed. Avoid having drawers attached to workbenches. These allow clutter to continue to be hidden. Without them there will be transparency.

3. *Clear Containment.* With the unnecessary rubbish removed, clearly define where everything else will be stored. Frequently used items should be stored closest to the cell on open shelves. Occasionally used equipment should be stored away from the cell, but still in a clearly identified and defined location.

4. *Cell Charts.* There must be a suite of productivity and quality measures

generated for the cell to show how it is performing. Calculation sheets for both productivity and right-first-time rates need to be prepared for the cell members to use: they must be easy to understand and quick to perform. To begin with, it might be better for just one operator to be nominated to perform the calculations and update the charts. Updating the charts with pen and ruler each day may make them get soiled or torn with time; so, at the start of each new month, the charts should be replaced with electronically updated revisions from the supervisor's master spreadsheet.

5. *Cell Discipline.* Once the cell has run for a few weeks, and the exact number and position of the benches has been concluded with certainty, the boundaries and entrance to the cell need to be defined. There are many colors of tape or paint that can be used on the floor to define these different cell features. It is also necessary to mark the floor with the location of any boxes of materials that are allowed to sit there. If a tray of work will always sit in a particular place on a workbench, then that too should be marked using a rectangle of colored floor tape. These marked out locations are called "foot-prints." Whether floor tape or paint is used, the same colors for each classification should be universally used across the entire factory.

The Housekeeping Audit Process

Once the lean cell has been created and the lean leap in housekeeping standards has been made, there is significant risk that the area will slip backward in its standards, rather than going on to improve still further. If something needs to be improved, the first step is to start monitoring it to discover where additional improvements can be made. In so doing, the employees will realize that it is a matter of importance. I recommend you use a housekeeping audit check-sheet similar to the one shown in **Figure 15.1**. Use it on a fortnightly basis to begin with, but when the lean cell is mature, a monthly check should be sufficient.

Depending on your specific factory, products, and processes, you will want to alter the criteria to fulfill your needs. Every one of the audit measures needs to be totally believed in—any measures that you don't feel this way about should be customized so that they are important to your own manufacturing process. Retain the challenge of high standards of attainment: otherwise the audit will make it too easy to achieve high scores, and it will be a waste of time.

The criteria are grouped into several bands, and, like a traffic light system,

CELL/AREA:	Red Cell	DATE:	Week 24

STAGE		AUDIT CRITERIA	0	1	2	3	4	5	COMMENTS
"Red Light"	Clear Out Chaos	Anything unnecessary in work area? Parts, tools?						x	
		Any bits, trimmings, fluff, on floor?				x			
		Broken equipment, damaged chairs or benches?						x	
		How many hiding places exist for clutter?					x		
		Sufficient rubbish bins available?						x	
		Cleaning material available & stored on shadow-board?						x	
"Yellow Light"	Clear Containment and Cell Charts	Cell boundaries and entrance marked out & not chipped?					x		Yes available, no shadow-board yet
		Seldom used tools/parts located close by & identified?		x					
		Gangways around cell marked out & unobstructed?			x				
		To what extent does the area have & use a display board?					x		
		No soiled notices, every displayed chart up-to-date?						x	
		Is it easy to see if things are missing?			x				
		All work documentation protected, filed, available?			x				
		Cleaning rota on display, in use, and uses only 1 person?				x			Yes, but needs to be done smarter
"Green Light"	Class Act Coordination	All safety risks identified?						x	
		Does parts storage system include auto-replenishment?			x				Metal yes, electronics no
		Preventive Maintenance sheets in use?	x						No, & it's needed for K3000 m/c
		Fire extinguishers & escape routes clearly defined?		x					
		Does cell have real identity, color, pride, visual impact?						x	
		Are there visually effective training sheets aids?	x						V. Poor
		Subtotals:	2	2	8	6	12	35	

TOTAL SCORE: 63 /100 = 63%

Figure 15.1. The 5-S housekeeping audit.

they help to indicate how far along good housekeeping's evolutionary journey the cell has traveled. If you start an audit without a housekeeping blitz, it's likely that the first audit score will be embarrassingly low. Even with a blitz, you should expect some low scores to start with; it's nothing to be ashamed of. What we are really looking for over a period of time is *improvement.* Cell housekeeping rivalries shouldn't be based on which cell has the highest scores. They should be based on the *greatest rate* of improvement (this also applies to productivity and quality). During cell meetings, make a point of praising cells that have improved their graph trends.

Who should do the auditing? You can't ask people to audit their own areas, for obvious partisan reasons. Using an operator from one area to audit another cell will also lead to compromises. There is potential for the person not to clearly understand the criteria expectations, and he/she won't want to upset any friends they have in the neighboring cell that they are auditing. If you ask a team leader or a supervisor to audit another person's area, even they are likely to mark it too high or too low. Either they will be kind, hoping to receive similar high marks in a "I'll scratch your back if you'll scratch mine" kind of way, or they'll be too tough on what they see as the "competition." One of the other difficulties is achieving consistent marking standards—only with consistency will you be able to look at the housekeeping graph and know for sure if the cell has gotten better or worse.

Instead, it is advisable to use someone bright, fair, and as impartial as you can find, and coach him/her into fully understanding what the audit is trying to achieve. If there are lots of areas to audit, this can take up a lot of time, but one fair outsider will apply things consistently. Be totally clear that he or she must be impartial and that overmarking to avoid upsetting anyone will in fact not be helpful. Apply some degree of randomness to when the audits will take place and in what order—if the timing of an audit is very predictable, the cell members will soon fall into the habit of having a special tidy-up just before they expect to be checked. Finally, the audits must be at least as frequent as the cell meeting schedule, as the shortcomings from the most recent audit will be one of the many things requiring discussion for improvement suggestions. An example of a long-term graph for mapping improvement is illustrated in **Figure 15.2**.

The Need for a Cell Cleaning Rota

A specified order of rotation for cleaning duties is beneficial to the housekeeping audit for two very good reasons. First, it clearly nominates a

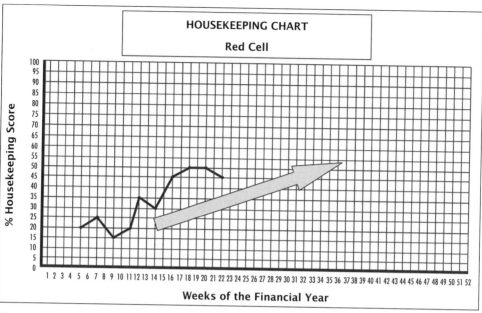

Figure 15.2. A housekeeping chart showing bi-weekly audit scores.

specific person to clean the cell on that particular day or for that particular week. Without a rota, the risk is that everyone will shirk their responsibilities. Anybody can clean up and someone has to, but unless individuals are nominated *in writing*, it is likely that it just won't get done.

Second, because cleaning is usually done at the end of the shift, it can sometimes be used as an excuse for everyone to stop early. But it is not necessary for the whole cell to stop work while this happens—to do so only results in valuable output minutes lost. However, if only one person stops (because you have an agreed system), you have a legitimate reason to expect less wasted production time.

The cleaning rota can include all cell members (see **Figure 15.3**), but if one/two of the people are already performing productivity and quality calculations, it may be fairer that they be excused from the cleaning rota.

Good Housekeeping Summary

Good housekeeping is based on high levels of visibility, transparency, and transferability. A good philosophy to use is the saying "a place for everything, everything in its place." Nothing should be present that isn't used, and anything that is used should have a clearly identified storage location.

To many people, good housekeeping may seem to be a minor, qualitative

Red Cell Cleaning Rota													
Week Number:	1	2	3	4	5	6	7	8	9	10	11	12	13
Julie Kinver	✔			✔			✔			✔			✔
Sue Torrence		✔			✔			✔			✔		
Chris Coles			✔			✔			✔			✔	

Figure 15.3. A cleaning rota chart for a cell.

issue, but it produces some very valuable and quantifiable benefits. Instead of the shop floor always needing an emergency clean-up every time some customers visit the factory, the workplace becomes a world-class facility that maintains a permanent tour-ready status.

Chapter 16

Key Performance Indicators for Lean Cells

The Skills Matrix

A skills matrix is essential in each cell to show:

- what skills are required to work in the cell
- which people usually (and occasionally) work there
- to what degree each individual is trained in each different skill.

If the list also includes operators that have worked in the cell from time to time, it serves as a useful reminder for a supervisor as to which other operators can be brought into the cell when the regular crew finds itself short-handed.

This record of skills is far more useful and visible than a set of records in the personnel office that would be constantly out of date, and too remote and inaccessible to be of any practical use. During a cell meeting, the present level of skills should be on the agenda for discussion. The matrix will show where there are areas for improvement. Once highlighted, these training requirements can be listed on the cell's "Improvement Actions" list, and nominated trainers can set date targets for the completion of training assignments. A typical skills matrix is shown in **Figure 16.1**.

Charting Productivity Calculations

Productivity is a very important measurement to have in a manufacturing environment. Traditionally, this has been purely for one reason—cost control. In a modern/lean facility, there are many indirect issues at play with this performance measurement, in addition to ensuring that budgeted profit margins are achieved.

Involving the cell members in the cell's measurement, recording, and reporting brings the team a high degree of ownership over their own performance. Cell productivity should be calculated at the end of each day, or, if applicable, at the end of each shift. When the work team performs

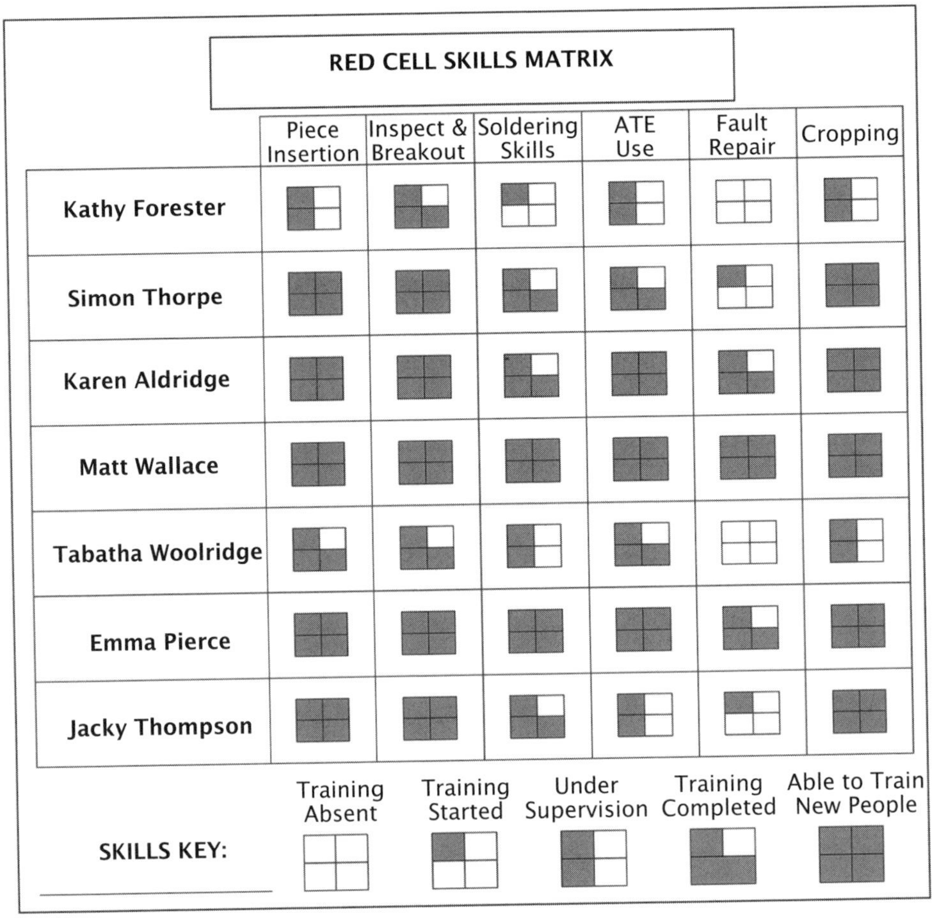

Figure 16.1. A cell's skills matrix chart.

self-measurement, extremely beneficial changes in attitude will occur. The team will:

• want to off-load surplus operators if the loading demand on the cell is being met

• want the best operators in their own cell, putting pressure on peers to 1) get trained properly on all the jobs, and 2) work at a good pace so the team does not end up carrying them

• start to take pride in how hard the team has worked each day

• take issue with any poor equipment or lack of correct tooling

• understand that reworking rejects directly affects the productivity score, and therefore every effort must be made to continuously eliminate the causes of rejects.

In order to know the manufacturing cost for each product that the factory makes, in addition to material costs, the organization will have documented labor times for each stage of product manufacture. Such operation times are arrived at by closely observing operators at work, and are traditionally known as "time-and-motion" studies. Whether these times include break times or not isn't important, because we are interested in the relative improvement or deterioration in productivity over time. All that really matters is that there is consistency between the work-study rules and the way the daily calculation will be done.

The productivity percentage is the ratio of hours produced over labor hours used; and for this calculation to work, the units of measure need to be the same. Because it is much simpler for operators to estimate the total amount of labor used in their cell each day in terms of hours, the cumulative labor time for each product variant needs also to be stated in hours. This is also known as the "standard hours" for the product.

At this stage there is something else to consider. Psychologically, it is more challenging for a team to be striving to reach a 100% level. If a team is achieving productivity levels of *over* 100%, this makes it appear that they are exceeding the level of effort that was expected by management, and the motivation to do better will be weak. I strongly recommend that, where necessary, official standard times should be factored down by a factory-wide 30% to get this scenario working in favor of continuous improvement.

The productivity calculation:

$$\frac{\text{number of units} \times \text{standard hours each}}{\text{hours of labor used}} = \% \text{ productivity}$$

or:

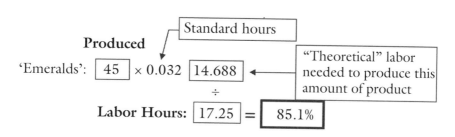

Inevitably, however, an individual cell will produce a number of different product variants, and each probably has slightly different standard times. This makes the calculation slightly more involved:

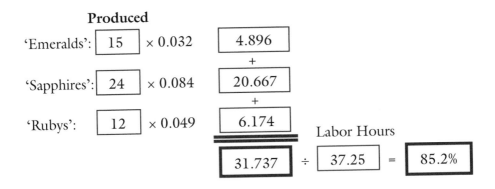

The calculation sheet needs to be kept as simple as possible, keeping in mind that the operator performing the calculation won't be a mathematician. The easier it is to make the calculations, the easier it will be to find someone happy to be nominated to perform them. The simpler the sheet, the less risk there is that the score will be calculated incorrectly. A typical error would be to misunderstand the decimal places in the standard time for a product, or to write down 34 $\frac{1}{2}$ hours as 34.3 (instead of 34.5), for example. Take the time to coach the nominated cell member to get it right, and don't be tempted to give up and do it yourself. For an outsider to tell the team how they have done will take away the ownership over their own performance.

Included in the total labor time should be any rework carried out on rejects, time for on-the-job training, and time used to perform housekeeping chores such as part replenishment or cleaning. Do not include any absence for holidays, sickness, passouts, cell meetings, briefings, or external training sessions.

It is then a short step to multiply this easy-to-follow layout so that a whole week's worth of productivity calculation, as seen in **Figure 16.2**, can be held on one sheet of paper. Copies of these productivity calculation sheets, individually designed for each different cell, can then be distributed to each area on clipboards. The person who is nominated to calculate productivity needs to make a log of who worked in the cell throughout the day. Several of the people will have been in the cell all day, but one person might have had to leave early for a doctor's appointment, or an outsider may have joined the cell mid-morning and stayed till the end of the day. It will be easy to forget such movement of people unless the nominated individual records it *as it happens*.

Calculating the cell's productivity is very important to do on a daily basis in order for the cell team to receive frequent feedback on how they are doing. If each day's results are plotted daily on the productivity chart, I find that

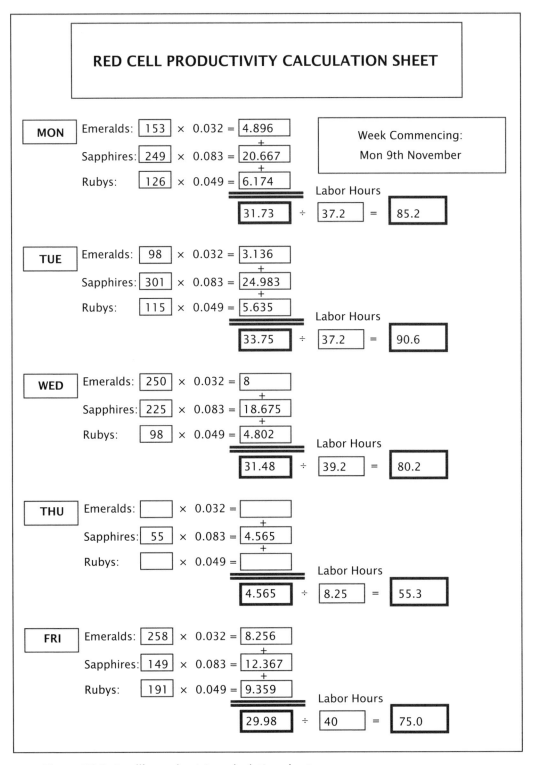

Figure 16.2. A cell's productivity calculation sheet.

there is too much data and the chart becomes unreadable. My preference is to plot an average cell productivity for the whole week and update the chart on that basis.

At the start of a new week, a supervisor collects the completed sheets from the week before, and the data for the week are averaged. While doing this, be on guard for a very common mistake: adding up the five days results and then dividing by five. Doing this on the given example on the previous page, where the five days scores were 85.2%, 90.6%, 80.2%, 55.3%, and 75.0%, would appear to give an average of 77.26%.

The correct way to calculate the week's overall productivity is to divide the sum of the produced hours by the sum of the labor hours used. This allows the "weight" of the results to be considered. The 55% day, for example, was just one person, and it should carry less weight than busier days.

These weekly averages are then added to the spreadsheet that is used to update all the charts, and new charts are printed out to supersede the previous ones on display. Honesty plays a big part in getting operators to perform productivity scoring: it might be quite tempting to forget the hours of overtime that were performed before the usual starting time, etc. Be on the lookout for results that are too consistent to be believable and, if necessary, check to confirm that the data are genuine.

The productivity chart should contain sufficient weeks of historical performance for it to clearly show a trend; so, at the start of a new year, I recommend that eight weeks of data from the end of the previous year should be carried over. When you attempt this, you will find that computer generated spreadsheet charts don't like the weeks of data to go from 45 through 52 and then zero to 1, 2, 3, 4, for the following year. Instead, the week numbers will need to be deducted going backwards (this also applies to any other similar chart), i.e.:

Old Business Year Finishing   ▼   New Business Year Starting

Actual Week Number:	45	46	47	48	49	50	51	52	1	2	3	4	5	6	7	8
Numbers Needed to be Used:	-7	-6	-5	-4	-3	-2	-1	0	1	2	3	4	5	6	7	8

One feature that may be a useful addition to such a chart is a "Desired Trend Line" that can be drawn in by hand with colored pen and a ruler, or can be added electronically before printing out. This line needs to be realistic and sensible according to your own experience and judgment; it is there to be used for comparison to the real data.

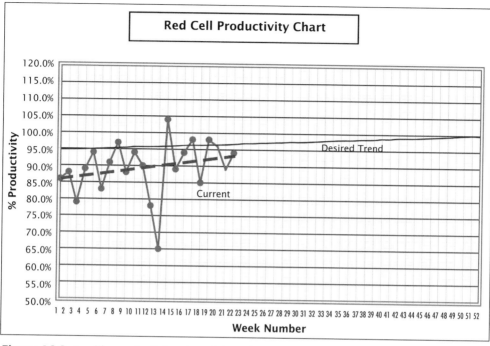

Figure 16.3. A cell's productivity chart (plotted weekly).

Another feature to add to the chart is a "Current Trend Line," which is a plotted line that bisects the scattering of points on the graph. It is often shown in green. If the spreadsheet can show this automatically, it can't be argued with, and it avoids any doubt about whether changes in the cell's performance over time have been improving or getting worse. **Figure 16.3** shows a productivity chart with trend lines in place.

The Right-First-Time (RFT) Calculation and Chart

Quality is another key measure for the cell, and there are many ways of recording it. Separate from any statistical process control (SPC), a quality measure and chart should be maintained to show historically how the cell has been performing. The recommended method for doing this is to measure/record Right-First-Time, i.e., the first time pass-rate. Why *first time* pass-rate? You will often find that a reworked component/product is more likely to fail than a unit that is about to be tested for the first time. It is also misleading to record that a single unit has failed the same test several times, and doing so will skew the results unfavorably. It is therefore recommended that tests on reworked units are not added to the record sheets—either as *another* unit or as *another* reject.

Product Nonconformance Record Sheet

Collecting right-first-time data is a matter of recording how many new/fresh/never-before-tested units failed a test compared to how many new units in total were tested (excluding rework tests). See **Figure 16.4**. With some tests, the result is either a pass or a fail. But in many assembly areas, for instance, there may be several different ways in which the failed unit has been unable to meet the required standards (failure modes). When this is the case, a more detailed record of the failures can be collected allowing enough data to create a Pareto chart as well. (A Pareto chart is a bar chart arranged from high to low, in order to reveal, instantaneously, which problems should be addressed first.)

On every bench within a cell where an operator is testing product, there should be a Test Record Sheet—best held on a clipboard—on which a tally chart record of tests and failures that occur throughout the day can be recorded. See **Figure 16.8** for an example of a Pareto Chart used in this manner.

The RFT% Calculation

With productivity, there needs to be just one calculation and chart per cell, irrespective of whether there are one or more products being produced. With quality, if the cell produces several different products, then each of them will need its own unique RFT% calculation sheet and separate chart. Only if the products being made are almost identical variants of each other is it acceptable for there to be a combined RFT% calculation and chart. Grouping reject data from different products into one measure is pointless, as you lose clarity about which products need the urgent attention from problem-solving teams, and which don't.

It must be a rule of the cell that all rejects are reworked and repaired within the cell before the day is over. This helps to identify the reject causes very soon after they were made, helping to determine ways to prevent those failure modes from recurring. It also prevents reject levels building up. The calculation is:

$$\frac{\text{(Number of good ``new'' units finished in the cell)} - \text{(Number of first-time rejects)}}{\text{Number of good ``new'' units finished in the cell}} = \% \text{ RFT}$$

On a Monday, the leading hand collects up all the previous week's test record sheets from their clipboards and inputs the data into a preprepared spreadsheet. This allows the tabulated information to be manipulated into a more meaningful and organized manner so that it can now be used as part of a management report. This work is highly suited to a computer spreadsheet

DODGER REJECT RECORD		Week 1						Week 2						Week 3						Week 4					
		M	T	W	T	F/S	Totals	M	T	W	T	F/S	Totals	M	T	W	T	F/S	Totals	M	T	W	T	F/S	Totals
	QUANTITY PRODUCED:	56	43	57	55	45	**256**	34	67	45	35	8	**189**	96	34	98	12	87	**327**	88	74	98	81	69	**410**
FAILURE MODE	Battery fault							I				I	**2**		I				**1**	I					**1**
	Dead		I	I			**2**		I				**1**											I	**1**
	Functions incorrect				I		**1**																		
	Missing LCD segments		I			I	**2**		I	I	II		**4**	I		I		I	**3**		I				**1**
	Missing component																					II			**2**
	Damaged cover																								
	Ghosting LCD																								
			2	1	1	1	**5**	1	2	1	2	1	**7**	1	1	1		1	**4**	1	1	2		1	**5**

Additional Notes and Comments:

Figure 16.4. A record sheet for rejects (to be mounted on a clipboard and filled in by the operator "live").

DODGER REJECT REPORT	Totals	% of Built	% of Rejects	Week No: 1	2	3	4	5	6	7	8
FAILURE MODE / PRODUCED	2,468			256	189	327	410	289	343	278	376
Missing LCD segments	18	0.7%	42.9%	2	4	3	1	2	1	3	2
Dead	8	0.3%	19.0%	2	1		1		2	1	1
Functions incorrect	5	0.2%	11.9%	1				1	2	1	
Battery fault	4	0.2%	9.5%		2	1	1				
Missing component	4	0.2%	9.5%				2	1			
Ghosting LCD	2	0.1%	4.8%					1			1
Damaged cover	1	0.0%	2.4%						1		
	42	1.7%	100.0%	5	7	4	5	5	6	5	5
Weekly Reject %:				2.0%	3.7%	1.2%	1.2%	1.7%	1.7%	1.8%	1.3%
RFT%				98.0%	96.3%	98.8%	98.8%	98.3%	98.3%	98.2%	98.7%

A Pareto chart can be produced using this data, but first sort all the rows (3-9) into decreasing magnitude of the values in the second column.

An X-Y Scatter chart (with added trend line) can be produced using this part of the spreadsheet.

Figure 16.5. A reject summary spreadsheet.

because prewritten equations perform the required calculations on the data quickly and efficiently. In having the information on a spreadsheet, you also make it very simple to turn the data into charts (**Figure 16.5**).

Although we wish to gather the information on rejects daily because it gives the cell an immediate feedback on the day, when it comes to publishing a chart or table with this daily information, there will be too much "noise" and the data will be misleading. It therefore needs to be accumulated into weekly groupings (**Figure 16.6**), with perhaps monthly summaries. Only when this happens will the information become statistically relevant and the true underlying trends revealed.

The Failure Mode Tally Chart

If data is important, then it should be measured. Don't measure data unless you are going to make a record of it. Don't record it unless you are going to present it in a meaningful way to people (a table or a chart). And don't publish the data unless you are going to take improvement actions on the basis of its results. In other words, analyze data only to the level that is necessary. If you know that you have only the resources to attack reject causes on the two biggest running products, then have RFT% calculations and charts for all the products, but only publish Pareto charts for the two biggest runners.

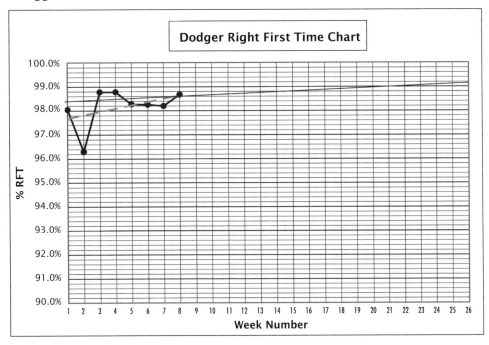

Figure 16.6. A Right First Time (RFT) chart.

Finally, on the matter of product quality, to aid the definition and resolution of the failure modes, a key tool is to make a tally chart of the two biggest failure modes (**Figure 16.7**). This is best done only on large running product lines where efforts in reject reduction will reap the largest rewards. Do it for an entire diverse product range and you are likely to get into "paralysis by analysis," and kaizen action resources will be spread too thinly. **Figure 16.8** shows a Pareto chart detailing the relative magnitude of all the Dodger reject modes.

Tally Chart of Dodger's 2 Largest Failure-Mode Repair Analysis

Missing LCD segments	18	COMMENTS & SUGGESTIONS
Dirty elastomeric strip	‖‖ ‖‖	i)talk to supplier, ii)wipe 1st with lint free cloth
Damaged carbon pads	‖‖ I	i)check our handling first, ii)talk to supplier
PCB track damage	‖‖	Caused at breakout -train on best technique
Dead	8	COMMENTS & SUGGESTIONS
Missing Terminals	I	Alter jig so if terminal missing, found earlier
Open Circuit	II	Dry joints -ensure flow solder monitored.
Wrong slide switch used	‖‖	Ensure storage system is corrected to prevent
Blown VDR		mix-ups, poke-yoke?

Figure 16.7. An additional data collection sheet allows the cell to more closely monitor the two most frequent rejects experienced while assembling Dodger units.

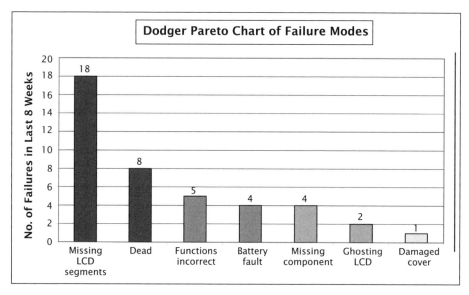

Figure 16.8. A Pareto chart showing all Dodger rejects.

The precise reasons for why a failure mode occurred are usually only found when the unit is repaired, and, if this valuable information is not recorded, then knowing how to reduce the reject levels becomes very difficult. The tally chart should be a prepared table, supplied on a clipboard to the person responsible for repairing on a daily basis the faulty units.

The Improvement Action Plan

Reporting all the previous charts is totally pointless unless the data is used to drive through improvement actions (**Figure 16.9**). The way to achieve this is to hold cell meetings on a periodic basis with each team, to praise any increases in performance, and also analyze any dips in performance. This must be done without blame. A drop in productivity is probably due to a malfunctioning piece of equipment or an increase in rejects, necessitating rework effort that left less time for production work. The cell team will find the various causes for a fall in productivity very frustrating, and will acknowledge that the problems are a waste of time that they could well do without. Correcting such problems will lead not only to better RFT rates but also improvements in productivity—everybody wins!

The Improvement Action List is where these problems can be addressed and resolved.

➤ List the problems—don't necessarily try to write down solutions in the cell meeting.

➤ Get input later from the production engineers and/or perform trials to test alternatives prior to planning the implementation of changes.

Red Cell Improvement Action Plan					
Problem	**Cause**	**Required Action**	Person Responsible	Date Requested	Status
Poor team mobility around cell limiting possible productivity	2 members need better soldering training so they can perform all the jobs like the others can.	Leading hand to run 'soldering school' sessions	Christine Fish	25 Oct.	Done
Transformers with bent legs take too much time to straighten & get in pcb	Inadequate packaging and heavy handling by supplier & delivery system.	Meet with supplier and show examples of problem. Improve packaging system.	Buyer	25 Oct.	In Progress
Low Housekeeping score	Nowhere to put dustpan, brush and broom.	Shadow-board required	L. Flatley	8 Nov.	No Action

Figure 16.9. A cell's improvement action plan.

> Write down who is going to be responsible for resolving the problem and taking action.

> State a planned completion date.

> Have a final column to show the status of the problem (no change, in progress, completed).

Collate all the different Improvement Action Lists from each of the cells, sort the actions by person responsible, and then sort the required actions into order of priority. In this way, the maintenance engineer has his own job list, as do the various production engineers and the materials manager. This is far more likely to generate the required improvement effort than would otherwise result.

Summary: The Visual Cell's Notice Board

The number of charts that will be produced may be at least ten, perhaps more. Too many charts will result in "chart-blindness," where no clear message can be read within a few moments. A four-foot-by-three-foot felt covered notice board will probably be required to hold this many sheets of paper.

Mounting the notice board on a wheeled stand with a white board on the reverse allows kanbans and cell charts to be displayed in the same place. The board (see **Figure 16.10**) can be wheeled to the cell meeting for discussion on the cell's performance, and wheeled back again afterwards.

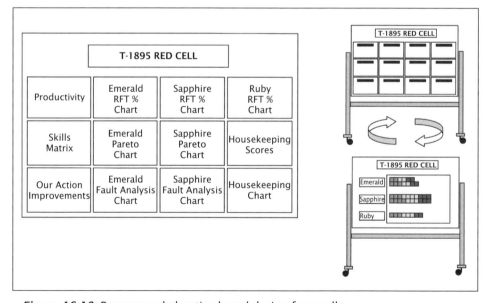

Figure 16.10. Recommended notice board design for a cell.

Chapter 17

Cell Meetings

Performing regular cell meetings is a very important function, and doing it well will help knit the cell operators together into an empowered team. Cell meetings can be used to drive forward improvements, thereby becoming the shop floor's "kaizen engine." Cell meetings are the mechanism to realize improvements in quality, productivity, and operator enthusiasm. Performing cell meetings and then *failing to act* on the suggestions they generate will have the negative effect of lowering morale. What would be the point in suggesting anything if nobody is listening? An absence of cell meetings can cause the operators to set their own agenda, which could also worsen productivity and quality levels.

The Cell Meeting Agenda
Like any meeting, in order to get the best out of it, a general agenda should be followed.

1. Discuss the kanban board and the level of work in the cell, as indicated by the relative number of tickets present. Has it been in the red all week, or in the green? Is the cell going to get busier or will the work decline? Does the cell currently contain the right number of operators? Will this number be changing over the coming weeks?

2. What have the productivity scores been like recently? Is the direction of change + or -? Are there big performance fluctuations throughout the week? These might be signs of poor work flow or the occurrence of special cause rejects. What caused the bad days?

3. Quality scores (right first time %) for each product: trends, problems, issues.

4. Skills matrix: is it up to date? Is enough progress being made? What commitments to people learning new skills can be agreed to and completed for next time?

5. Housekeeping scores: how is the cell doing? What are the main shortfalls in attaining even better scores?

6. What's been the progress with the actions listed since the last meeting?

7. What new suggestions to combat the recent quality problems, material issues, tooling problems, etc., are there?

8. Discuss any other matters of business.

Cell Meeting Style

The style of a cell meeting, as well as its frequency and duration, will vary according to the situation. If a cell has just been created, it will need very frequent and intensive cell meetings with much time put aside to discuss how operators should move around the cell flexibly, encouraging the continuous flow of work. If the cell has been running for six months, the operators will have understood their role and will have started to feel frustrated each time they hit days of poor quality that knock their productivity score down. During this period, they will need regular meetings to pinpoint the causes of their problems, and to generate solutions that will combat them.

When the cell is over 12 months old, it has a greater degree of maturity, and the number of suggestions and improvements will start to slow. At this stage, the cell meetings can be allowed to become less frequent, and the top one or two causes of rejects that stubbornly persist need to be attacked in a more focused approach. The introduction of new equipment or alternative components will require more technical support than was needed before. After two years, the cell's culture will be mature enough to reduce the WIP further and thereby get the lead time down even more. Cell meetings for a team of 3–6 people should last between 20 and 30 minutes. The larger the cell, the more issues, the greater the number of topics to cover, and so the meeting will take longer.

The cell meeting is a marvelous opportunity to praise the cell members for their efforts in reducing rework, improving productivity, and broadening their skills. If rejects have temporarily increased, then you will need to ask why, but not in an angry way. Blame will only take the organization backwards and prevent continuous improvement. Nobody likes to produce bad work. However, people don't care unduly if bad work is produced when they feel that their superiors don't care. By charting quality and discussing it in cell meetings, management shows that it cares and the organization can harness the deep-rooted willingness of everyone to produce high quality work. If they think that they will be made to feel personally guilty for making mistakes, then problems will be covered up. Once this starts happening, root causes will become nearly impossible to find and define.

When the manager running the cell meeting asks for better productivity, the emphasis must be that this can be achieved by taking the frustrations and wastes out of the job, such as double-handling, delays, reject/rework effort, and poor information. If operators feel that management's agenda is just to make them work harder, then it is unlikely that anything will ever be gained. When they are listened to, and their problems are resolved, the team will feel empowered and morale will be high. When the cell takes ownership over its performance, and takes pride in what it has achieved, the team will no longer be happy to "carry" anyone and put up with bad habits—like people cherry-picking the best jobs, or individuals wandering off for a chat.

Dealing with Training Issues

For cells to work effectively, all of the operators will need to be capable of performing most of the jobs. This won't be the situation when the cell has just been created. It will take patience and a preparedness to endure a slight hit on productivity for a while, so that the essential cross training of operators can take place. The cell meetings can be used to organize this in a structured manner so that it is done bit by bit. Without such control, everyone will want to try a new job every day, the effectiveness of the training will be second rate, and the productivity will fall through the floor. Understand the operators' wishes—they will want to move around in the cell to a reasonable degree, especially if the jobs are boring. They will also want to see their skills matrix gradually filling up with black squares. The supervisor and the cell members need to agree to some ground rules at this point.

- How many training days does it take to learn each of the jobs, after which point the new skill is "signed-off" on the skill's matrix?

- How many people is it reasonable to have being trained at any one time so that the cell remains operationally effective?

Understanding these two issues allows a training plan to be defined to help the operational needs of the business, but with consideration toward fairness and opportunity. The team needs to agree to rotate people on different jobs to some sensible degree during the day/week, so that everyone's skills stay sharp and the training isn't forgotten. This can be left as a verbal understanding.

The Reality of Cell Improvement

It is impossible for production engineers designing the new cell to get it perfect straight away, especially if they have not yet fully understood the principles of lean. This said, the best approach is to ensure that the basics of the cell design are sound, and then to move the benches and machinery without excessive procrastination. Everyone needs to accept that there will be a period after implementation where the rough edges of the cell's initial design will need to be knocked off using an intensive series of cell meetings with the support from engineering/maintenance.

Planning the engineering resources to be available to make these adjustments is just as important as getting the benches moved in the first place. If this finishing off does not occur, then the cell will never be successfully completed. It may appear to outsiders that the cell looks finished, but the operators will know that it isn't functioning as it should. You can't risk leaving the job half-done, with the operators feeling frustrated. The organization would decide that, without a successful conclusion to their first attempts at U-shaped cells, lean "doesn't work here." Make sure the engineers who will be required to oversee the cell improvements set aside enough time for this workload during the month that follows the implementation.

The Improvement Action Plan in Detail

After each cell meeting, the action plan needs to be updated with any new information. To allow evidence that activities do get finished, completed actions should be kept on the sheet until the following meeting. Unless an

Red Cell Action Plan				14 August 2003
Problem	**Action**	Person Responsible	Completion Date	Complete?
Jill Copse (blade prep) on maternity	Robbie to train on job for 2 weeks	Jill Copse	24th August	
Motor rivet press is inconsistent	Maintenance to overhaul	John Norris	3rd September	✔
Delivered metal stampings rusty	Purchasing to discuss with supplier and to ensure are degreased only just before delivery	Sue Parsons	3rd September	
Housekeeping difficult because screws roll onto floor	Maintenance to fill in gaps between benches with boarding	John Norris	14th September	
LCD's are ghosting	Change resistance values	Andy Beadle	3rd September	✔

Figure 17.1. An example of a cell's Action Plan.

Improvement Action Plan is used, the information gets left to memory and the cell has no way of displaying what its development actions are. Also, it is an excellent way to motivate the individuals who should be carrying out the necessary work, and to commit them to completing their actions within a reasonable time frame. **Figure 17.1** shows a sample Action Plan.

Chapter 18

Planning and Scheduling Methods

Traditional Production Scheduling

Having large stocks of finished goods (FG) is a traditional method used to act as a buffer against forecasting errors and the limited flexibility of big-batch production. Additionally, if the market exhibits demand variability (and what market doesn't?), then surplus production capacity gets used filling up the FG store during quiet periods, with the intention that these stocks can be used to offset any shortfalls in production capacity during busier times. Monthly production plans are drawn up to take into account both the forecasted sales for each product and the stocks held in the FG store. Production's task is simply to build to that plan progressively across the month, allowing the planners and supervisors to batch work up into large runs without feeling that they need to worry about starving customers of any one product type. Of course, late and partial shipments still occur because people get complacent that the buffer will always protect them. Because counting such large stock holdings is too onerous a chore to do on a regular basis, significant changes in product demand regularly catch the operation by surprise.

When the demand for a particular product increases beyond the rate forecast, warehouse stocks decline, sometimes to a point where customers can no longer be supplied on time. During the next month, the build plan for that particular product would be increased to replenish the stocks back to reasonable levels. For some products, the reverse situation happens, but, either way, production will always seem to be out of step with the actual trends in demand. It is easy to see why there seems to be only one way of minimizing the risks of being unable to service customers demand—by keeping even larger stocks of finished product.

Traditionally, salesmen are praised for bringing in big orders. This can have a considerable effect on encouraging extra large spikes in demand to occur, a self-inflicted amplification that places even more difficulty on production. Traditional directors try to maximize the end-of-month figures, especially at the end of the half-year and at the end of the full year. This causes orders to be pulled forward from the beginning of the next month and into the end of the current one. This, in turn, causes further self-inflicted feast-or-famine cycles. Once orders have been pulled forward, it becomes a very difficult habit to stop, so for years the company will suffer from too many orders in the last week of the month, followed by a very quiet start to the next month. This all adds to the belief that finished stock holdings should be inflated to even greater quantities.

Ironically, traditional materials purchasing patterns are such that in the last week of the month, materials requests are sat on, and double quantities are then ordered as soon as the new month begins. This attempt to show the month-end stock figures in the best possible light actually adds to the reasons for material stockouts and partial assembly, resulting in lost productivity and WIP increases. The amplification of order spikiness (size variability) makes it very difficult for a production facility to be effective; the end losers are both the customers and the manufacturer. The good news is that with education and willingness, this amplification can be removed over time—once production can prove that it can flexibly and reliably work to reduced lead times. **Figures 18.1** through **18.3** show how a "natural" customer demand pattern becomes more and more spikey as "big order" and "pulling forward" activities are superimposed.

Benefits and Problems with Traditional Production Scheduling

The benefit to the organization of carrying large amounts of FG stock is to provide a solution to the limitations of an inflexible big batch production system. The traditional organization is also geared toward buying materials in monthly, though sometimes weekly, consignments. The build instructions

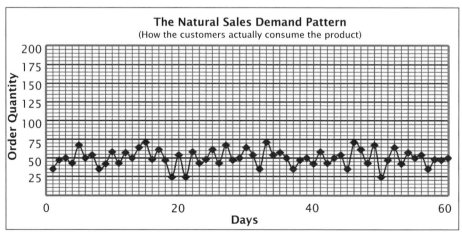

Figure 18.1. The natural sales demand pattern (how customers *actually* consume product).

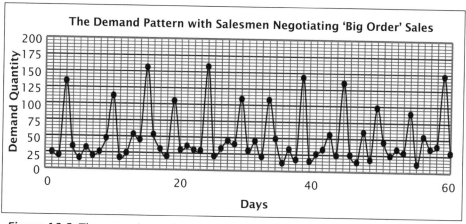

Figure 18.2. The same demand pattern with salesmen negotiating "big order" sales.

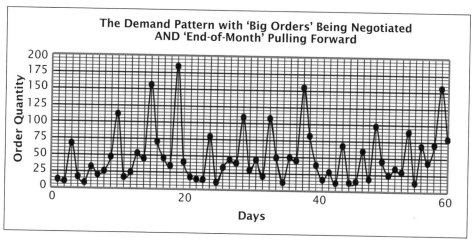

Figure 18.3. The demand pattern with big orders being negotiated *and* end of month orders pulling forward.

issued to the various areas of the shop floor are all interlinked and rely on the information coming from regular WIP counts. They also rely on the assumptions that 1) the correct materials come in from the suppliers on time, and 2) that large batches of work won't be rejected anywhere along the system. In real life, problems and complications inevitably occur, making it impossible to avoid some shipments being delayed.

Planning the shop floor in this traditional way leads to high costs. Holding material stock in its finished state, as opposed to its raw state, means that all of the labor costs associated with the product are tied up in addition to the material cost. Producing product that is not for immediate sale leads to negative cash flow—materials that have to be paid for are being consumed, but the activities on those materials are not leading to an immediate invoiceable sale. Traditional accounting comes to the rescue, as WIP is expensed as an asset to the company rather than a liability (when, in fact, we all know that the reverse is true).

This traditional method of planning can be described as a "push-system," where the instructions on what to build, in what quantities, and with what urgencies are directed first to the primary processes (the beginning of the production system), but also to some degree to the middle and final operations. Because of the WIP involved at every stage, this creates a complicated planning process that is inherently prone to misjudgments and mistakes, even when it is automated as far as possible with an MRP II software package.

Computers are often heralded as the solution to problems, but, in controlling production within factories, they would not be required if things were as simplified as they could be. Computers can, in fact, be just another potential liability to the organization each time the system/ network crashes.

Modern Scheduling Methods for Lean Manufacturing

If measured against a traditional factory, the lean operation, by definition, does not appear to operate with significant stocks of material: either work in progress or finished goods. Production scheduling techniques, therefore, have to be significantly different.

Once a lean cell has been designed, how will it know what products or product variants to make and in what quantity? When several cells are

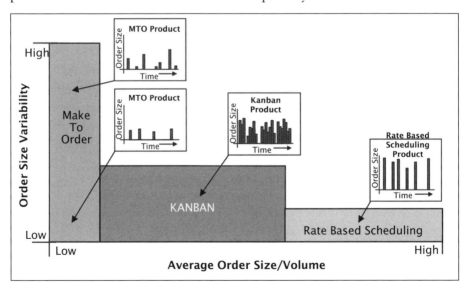

Figure 18.4. How volume variability characteristics determine the ideal scheduling method.

created, how will these islands of continuous flow be connected? There are several options—the most chic being kanban systems—but kanbans are only appropriate when the product demand patterns fit within a certain range. For any products lying on either side of that range, there are better methods to use: either Make-to-Order (MTO) or Rate-Based Scheduling (RBS) should be considered. **Figure 18.4** helps to demonstrate when each would be used.

Kanban Control

Kanban control has already been discussed in previous chapters, so you should be relatively familiar with it by now. It utilizes a small-to-moderate amount of WIP to act as a buffer and to prime the system. In addition, it employs a visual ticket system, with a kanban board, or sometimes work footprints on the floor, or vertical footprints on a backboard against which bins of material are stacked. The amount of stock that is designed into the kanban depends on two things.

1. What customer service level (the degree to which complete and on-time deliveries can be guaranteed) is required? If the company wishes to guarantee every customer, irrespective of order size, will always receive their shipment on time, then it needs to hold infinite stocks of finished goods. This would be nonsense, of course, so, instead, a compromise has to be decided upon. Is a 95% service level okay, or would a 98% service level be the norm for the market the company is in?

2. How readily is the manufacturing system able to replenish stocks that have just been consumed before the next order comes along? The more flexible the cell is in changing from one product to the next, and the more elastic the cell's build capacity, the easier it will be for it to rapidly replace stocks. Rapid stock replacement allows lower kanban stocks. A more inflexible set of circumstances will require greater kanban stocks.

Demand Characteristics

Kanban control is appropriate for products that: 1) need building on a regular basis, e.g., nearly every day, 2) are produced in reasonable volumes, and 3) exhibit "spikiness" of demand that is not too great. If products are to be controlled by kanban, then the stocks, by their very nature, will be frequently moving and turning over. If you try to use kanban control for products with volume-variability characteristics outside of these patterns, then you would end up holding high levels of stock that would spend most of its time gathering dust.

Benefits and Problems

Because it involves holding some stock, kanban control is not a totally lean way to schedule work. However, it is an excellent compromise until the organization develops its supply-chain infrastructure to truly support lean, and it is a hundred times better than to continue to use traditional scheduling methods. The beauty of a kanban is that it:

1. only replenishes product lines that are being consumed,
2. automatically signals changes in work priority,
3. limits WIP building to agreed levels, and
4. helps to signal changes in required production capacity, e.g., manning levels.

A phrase that is very appropriate to use in conjunction with kanban control is "pull system." A pull system is where a "vertical" line of production cells build only what is necessary to replenish those products being consumed. The initial trigger for deciding what to build, in what quantity, and with what urgency, is triggered by the customer at the very tail end of the process (i.e., packing), and it is this trigger that pulls work through the operation.

Make-to-Order (MTO)

In many ways, MTO is a very lean way of scheduling work—far leaner than kanban, because it works in a way that avoids holding permanent levels of stock. The principle behind it is that the product is made only when the customer orders it, and in the exact quantity that is requested. As a newly received order is started, stocks are built up until the full consignment is prepared and can be shipped, but this is the only WIP that is in evidence. MTO products will be those that have very intermittent build periods. They are only built when required; otherwise, other products, perhaps kanban ones, are made instead. When a new MTO work instruction is issued, it takes priority over any kanban work that has degrees of stock to act as a buffer during the period that the MTO work is being built. When the number of units is relatively small, MTO instructions can be a single written job card as shown in **Figure 18.5**.

Figure 18.5. A make-to-order ticket.

If the MTO involves a greater number of units (enough to fill several work trays), a multiticket system can be used (**Figure 18.6**). By using multiple tickets for a larger order, the progress the team has made in filling that order becomes much more visible: i.e., how many tickets have been used up out of the total number.

To avoid the tickets becoming lost, a wallet or envelope can be used. As a tray of work is completed, the first ticket is put in the tray (to be discarded later), etc. This allows the leading hand to quickly check the number of tickets still in the wallet to know how far the MTO has progressed without having to make a WIP count. Supervision can have greater confidence that the exact number of units will be correctly assembled with the multiple ticket system, because it is easier for the operator to keep a tally on how many trays have been filled when a ticket gets put in each tray. Counting to 48 accurately sounds easy, but when there might be 5 minutes or so between each product being assembled, and the work might carry over into a different day or shift, it is more likely than not that the counting accuracy will soon go astray.

If every order were treated as a MTO instruction, it would become very difficult to organize production. With lots of MTO instructions floating around, which would take priority? If some of the product lines do suffer from spiky orders, and those lines were all MTOs and didn't have any kanban buffer stocks, then the factory would have no protection against

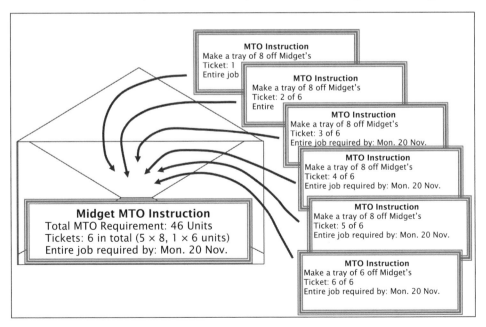

Figure 18.6. Using a multiple ticket make-to-order instruction.

sudden surges in customer demand. Having some product as kanban and some as MTO helps the enterprise to operate in a balanced and effective way.

If the majority of orders can be planned through a kanban pull system, then scheduling a few MTOs onto the factory becomes a highly practical thing to do. When it is decided which products will be classified as MTOs, then the team leader simply has to keep a lookout for when a customer orders any of those products. When this happens, he/she creates the MTO instruction card(s) and issues them at the right moment to the appropriate production cell.

Demand Characteristics

MTO build instructions are highly appropriate for any product that is sporadically required in low volumes and whose next order requirement is impossible to predict. You don't want to hold finished stocks of these "stranger" products—lines that are rarely required and seldom ordered. If you do, the stock may become damaged, mixed in with other lines, or may even hang around long enough to become obsolete.

Benefits and Problems

The benefit of MTO is clear: product manufacture without the requirement to hold stock. This is a lean dream; anybody wishing to sound really clever would say that all orders should be treated as MTO, and no product will be built unless there is an immediate sales requirement. In reality, where the company has a sales order pattern that has spikes, and there is little or no order smoothing being done, it is best to select only a few products of the right type to be MTO.

The main problem with MTO is that you can't do it unless either 1) the time it takes to build the full order is equal to or less than the customer lead time, or 2) the customer is okay waiting for the delivery however long it takes. Once the manufacturing system has developed further along the lean evolutionary road and the build time has become shorter because WIP queues have been removed, then more products can be transferred from kanban to MTO; but this will take time to realize.

Rate-Based Scheduling (RBS)

Rate-based scheduling is a system that uses a modest quantity of finished goods buffer stock to smooth out subtle fluctuations in customer demand. Because this will only be appropriate to a few products, these stocks will not be a considerable burden to the operation. To illustrate what RBS is, an example is required.

In this example, the customer is a company that manufactures domestic combi-boilers that include, among other things, heat exchanger plates that are fitted inside the boilers. The order pattern for the plates is remarkably stable, with an approximate delivery of 250 plates each week. The plates are shipped in plastic crates, 36 in each, and the customer returns the empty crates to the manufacturer a few days before the next shipment is needed. The order quantity ranges from 5 crates (180 plates) to 9 crates (324 plates), with the average being 7 (252 plates). This is a stable and predictable demand situation, and thus ideal for RBS control. RBS will benefit the company by allowing at least one of its products to be manufactured in a very stable manner.

Each day, the cell that fabricates these plates will be required to produce a steady 50–51 plates, putting them in a nearby storage rack. Each day the amount of stock held in the rack increases until the day that the delivery shipment is made, at which point the stock is reduced to a minimum level once again. This agreed minimum buffer stock is there just in case a high demand of 8–9 crates occurs for several consecutive weeks.

Calculating Stock Levels to Run an RBS System

The worst scenario that has to be accommodated is if the customer, for several unbroken weeks, places high orders. What buffer stock must be held prior to that run of high demand to ensure full shipments are achieved throughout those weeks? To evaluate this, you will need to look at an accumulation of many weeks of previous order-pattern information. Tabulate this in a way similar to the example method that follows, and start off with a "guessed" minimum stock (the stock that is left over in the racking after the most recent shipment has just been taken). Now, let the spreadsheet model what will happen over the course of several weeks of typical demand profile. The stock calculations are:

Next Week's *Maximum* Stock =
> Previous Week's Minimum Stock + RBS Weekly Production

Next Week's *Minimum* Stock =
> Maximum Stock (as calculated above) – Customer Demand

By using actual historical customer demand records in the table, and copying the formulae for minimum and maximum stock down the sheet, you get a mathematical model of how the stocks would fluctuate. The week's RBS production level should be set at the average weekly demand—in the example provided (**Figure 18.7**), this is 7 crates of 36 heat-exchanger plates (252 units). By adjusting the initial minimum stock, you will be able to evaluate at what point the customer never quite manages to empty the buffer stock completely and appears to always receive a complete and on-time shipment.

Once you have made the model show the sort of minimum stocks that will be needed, start off a new RBS system primed with 75% of the largest minimum stock that your post-balanced table of data shows. Do this because you won't know for sure whether the customer's current demand

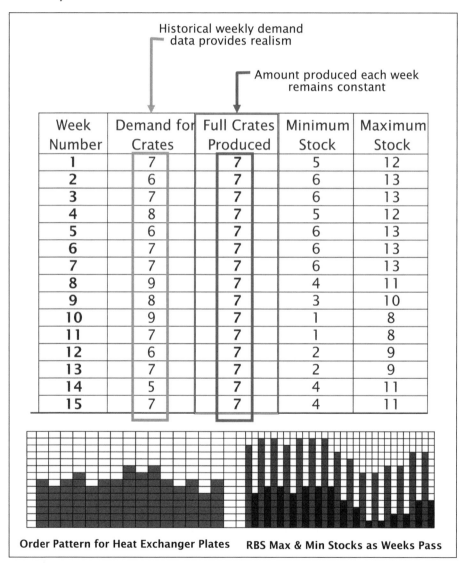

Historical weekly demand data provides realism

Amount produced each week remains constant

Week Number	Demand for Crates	Full Crates Produced	Minimum Stock	Maximum Stock
1	7	7	5	12
2	6	7	6	13
3	7	7	6	13
4	8	7	5	12
5	6	7	6	13
6	7	7	6	13
7	7	7	6	13
8	9	7	4	11
9	8	7	3	10
10	9	7	1	8
11	7	7	1	8
12	6	7	2	9
13	7	7	2	9
14	5	7	4	11
15	7	7	4	11

Order Pattern for Heat Exchanger Plates   RBS Max & Min Stocks as Weeks Pass

Figure 18.7. An example demonstrating rate-based scheduling.

is relatively high or relatively low compared to average demand. This will be a good level of buffer stock to start with, although you may wish to try reducing the minimum stock by a fraction after experience indicates that it looks to be too much.

Demand Characteristics

Use RBS only for products that sell in moderately high volume and have very predictable demand patterns. It would be inappropriate to use RBS for stable, low-volume product lines because it is easier to make such low volumes just-in-time and benefit from not holding stock. A production cell won't have difficulty making up small quantities at short notice.

Cells do, however, have considerable problems in guaranteeing that high volume orders ship on time if their production is left till the very last minute. Therefore, RBS is used and a constant daily quantity is produced throughout the week.

Benefits and Problems

One obvious reason that the customer will get a high level of service is that he is now protected from the risk of short or late deliveries because of the security of the RBS stock. However, the other main advantage is that by producing at such a stable rate all the time, component suppliers will find it far easier to provide a high level of delivery reliability because the company does not pass along any supply chain fluctuations. Lastly, by building at a constant rate, the administration and production control costs are reduced, production planning never has to be performed, and expediting effort is no longer required.

Determining What Planning Systems to Use for Which Products

It is imperative that the company correctly chooses which of the three scheduling techniques to use for each different product. In the process of deciding which of the alternatives to use, two criteria need to be known: 1) each product's average demand quantity, and 2) product demand variability (spikiness). Spikiness is defined by making a simple statistical analysis of sales data. To do this, a large amount of order history for each product needs to be made available; a period of 6 to 12 months of sales orders is about right. Once this data has been manipulated via a spreadsheet into the appropriate format, as shown in **Figure 18.8**, the data is easier to analyze. Relative spikiness is described by the ratio between the standard deviation for the data and the average daily demand.

	Average			Units Per Day Ordered By Customers												
Standard deviation	Daily Volume	sd/mean	PRODUCT	Day 1	Day 2	Day 3	Day 4	Day 5	Day 6	Day 7	Day 8	Day 9	Day 10	Day 11	Day 12	Day 13
12.51256	30	0.42141	Widget	23	16	35	25	19	54	12	31	37	42	45	29	18
11.91315	7	1.61324	Gadget	1	2	3	1	39	4	6	1	28	5	3	2	1
9.81822	83	0.11873	Smidger	95	78	67	88	91	93	73	82	94	79	82	66	87
5.063697	246	0.02057	Smoothey	250	250	250	250	240	240	250	250	240	240	250	240	250
6.572085	56	0.11784	Budget	55	69	58	57	55	49	52	60	45	48	54	64	59
10.2582	4	2.77826	Midget	0	0	0	36	0	0	0	0	0	12	0	0	0
9.74811	63	0.15417	Dodger	66	83	77	67	67	65	55	52	51	50	64	63	62
34.17958	107	0.31967	Seller	159	86	54	121	67	124	167	89	92	133	76	102	120

Figure 18.8. Daily volume variability data for eight fictitious products.

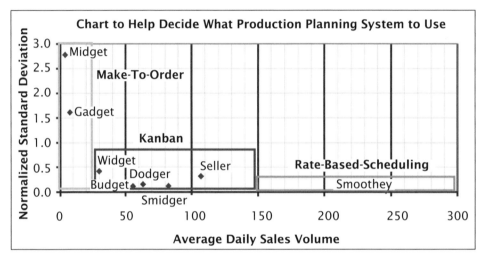

Figure 18.9. Charted results indicate which scheduling system is best for each product.

The table of data shows a range of different fictitious products, each one having its own unique order profile. As in real life, some are strangers and only sell every week or two, some are runners selling regular amounts each day. Some even fall in between—a few with highly variable order sizes, and some with very little variation in order size.

The next important thing to do is plot each of the products on a graph of Average Daily Sales Volume on the horizontal x-axis and with the spikiness ratio (standard deviation/average order size) on the vertical y-axis (**Figure 18.9**). Where the spikiness ratio is *less than 1.0*, kanbans might work okay. But kanbans work best with moderately high daily demand; less than 25 units, and it will be a bit pointless to hold kanban stocks. If the spikiness ratio is *less than 0.1* (which invariably goes hand in hand with high volumes), then RBS should be considered.

Products Appropriate for MTO Control: The calculations indicate that the *Midget* and *Gadget*, with their low average daily demand rate (because they are both strangers) and their high spikiness ratio, are MTO products.

Products Appropriate for RBS Control: Only the *Smoothey* product shows sufficient stability in order variability to be eligible for RBS control.

Products Appropriate for Kanban Control: There are five of the eight products that have a spikiness ratio between 1.0 and 0.1. These are *Widget*, *Budget*, *Smidger*, *Dodger*, and *Seller*. Production of these can be controlled with a kanban system.

The use of MTO and RBS has been discussed in some detail already, but products that are appropriate for control by kanban need further calculations, and preparation effort, before being handed over to the shop floor.

.

Chapter 19

Calculating Kanban Stock Levels

With the kanban products identified, calculations can now be made to decide stock levels for each of the products. These stocks will act as a buffer against a moderate degree of spiky demand, and will allow the pull system to be primed with a small amount of stock to allow enough time for replenishment to occur. These stock-sizing calculations can be "future proofed" for the coming 3–6 months by taking the spikiness measure arrived at from recent *historical* sales data and superimposing it onto the *forecasted* average daily demand for the months yet to come. In this way, the kanbans are sized appropriately to deal with any upward, downward, or perhaps seasonal demand variations.

The first thing that has to be done is to make a business decision about what level of customer service should be maintained. As discussed earlier, this is a question of significance because one cannot blindly state that customer service needs to be 100%: the only way to achieve that would be to have infinite levels of finished goods stock. However, a 90% level, i.e., 1 in 10 of your deliveries being either short or late, would be setting your targets very low indeed and would risk you losing orders to competitors. The sensible business reality is to choose a level somewhere between 95% and 99%. This decision comes down to a compromise between the amount of kanban stocks to be held and a customer delivery performance that is acceptable.

If a company sells some of its products in reasonable volumes, it is rational to assume that their demand patterns probably statistically fit the normal distribution. The normal distribution is a way to describe a particular type of natural variability; for example, the variability of people's height (to the nearest inch) from a group of 100+ individual men, all aged between 20 and 25 years old. When made into a bar chart of the number of people (Y-axis) against height *to the nearest inch* (X-axis), the highest bar will be at approximately 5'10", but either side of the height of each bar decreases in a bell-shaped curve. Assuming that sales volume variation for products follow this mathematical description, then some

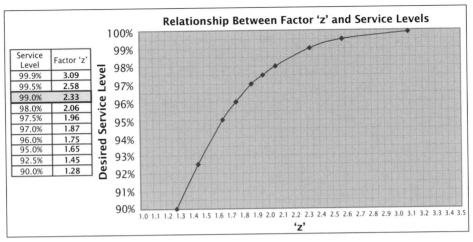

Figure 19.1. What "z" factor to use depending on what service level is chosen.

mathematical judgments can be made to help in our kanban sizing calculations.

The table and chart in **Figure 19.1** come from the statistical mathematics of a normal distribution. It is provided for referring to when you are making your own kanban calculations around your individual circumstances. In my example, we will plan for a customer service level of 99%, which means that the quantity "*z*" used in later calculations will be taken as a value of 2.33.

Clearly Defining the Factors Involved in Kanban Calculations

Historical Average Order Size = Once the data is grouped into the daily totals required by customers, over the course of the 3–12 months of data (e.g., 65–260 working days), what is the average order total per day for each product?

Lead Time = Number of days of WIP lag in the system, including changing materials, organizing a different print run, changing over an upstream supply system (i.e., how long does it take product to get through the build cells?).

Number of Days "Safety" =

$$\frac{(\text{Service Factor 'z'}) \times (\text{Std. Dev. of Historical Orders}) \times \sqrt{\text{Lead Time}}}{\text{Historical Average Order Size}}$$

Safety Stock = Number of days safety needed × *Expected* Average orders per day (using the sales forecast for the next 3 months).

Pipeline Stock = Lead Time (Days) × *Expected* Average orders per day (using the sales forecast for the next 3 months).

Kanban Size = Number of product units that will fit within the chosen tray/bin/box (not so many units or large a container that the number of kanbans is only one or two containers worth).

$$\text{Number of Kanban Tickets} = \frac{(\text{Safety Stock} + \text{Pipeline Stock})}{\text{Kanban Size}}$$

of which:

Number of Red Tickets =

$$\frac{(\text{Lead Time} \times \textit{Expected} \text{ Average Orders per Day})}{\text{Kanban Size}}$$

(Note: this is a rounded-up whole number)

Number of Yellow Tickets = (No. of Total Kanban Tickets − Red Tickets) / 2   *(Note: this is also rounded up to the nearest whole number)*

Number of Green Tickets = Total Tickets − No. of Red Tickets − No. of Yellow Tickets.

It is important to note that the kanban quantity includes working (pipeline) stock and also some safety stock. The pipeline stock quantity is based on average replenishment rates. The safety stock is sized to be large enough to buffer against spikes and the lead time delay for the cell to respond to a change in demand.

Never omit or ignore safety stock. Production life is never so simple as to assume that daily build or demand rates are always "average" and unchanging.

Never listen to opinions based on ignorance to reduce the kanban tickets by half, for example, because it looks as if only half the tickets are ever used. You would gain nothing financially, and you will simply upset the overall flexibility and rules that the kanban's calculations were designed around.

The kanban sizing calculations should be performed periodically every 3–6 months, even after the kanban has been designed and implemented. Some products will see sales grow, while others, toward the end of their product life cycle, may decline. As the sales team changes its emphasis toward encouraging smaller and more frequent orders, the spikiness will reduce, and the safety stock can be diminished.

	Day 1	Day 2	Day 3	Day 4	Day 5	Day 6	Day 7	Day 8	Day 9	Day 10	Day 11	Day 12	Day 13	Day 14	Day 15	Day 16	Day 17	Day 18	Day 19	Day 20	Day 21	Day 22	Day 23	Day 24	Day 25	Day 26	Day 27	Day 28	Day 29	Day 30	Day 31	Day 32	Day 33	Day 34	Day 35	Day 36	Day 37	Day 38	Day 39	Day 40	Day 41	Day 42	Day 43	Day 44	Day 45	Day 46
PRODUCT																																														
Widget	42	55	9	16	0	24	5	10	80	0	18	108	26	66	0	48	24	0	14	10	148	0	15	6	10	17	219	14	97	16	81	152	9	40	4	11	29	12	0	10	0	12	2	11	66	0
Smidger	69	43	0	56	34	118	28	57	45	39	43	0	35	112	23	54	134	35	0	45	121	23	16	0	25	19	0	12	31	37	42	0	29	18	0	16	0	25	19	54	12	31	37	0	59	129
Budget	55	1	129	57	55	0	52	60	178	18	54	64	6	55	69	58	0	55	87	52	60	9	48	54	64	3	78	48	54	0	0	55	23	52	4	45	87	54	0	59	45	48	0	64	0	47
Dodger	66	83	0	67	91	65	0	52	175	50	64	0	62	66	0	143	67	132	65	0	88	51	0	124	63	62	51	0	0	125	67	0	65	110	0	51	99	0	63	23	145	50	64	0	0	51
Seller	159	76	54	345	173	124	167	89	0	133	76	0	120	159	86	12	121	0	0	167	410	12	133	0	102	120	92	133	283	102	12	67	124	0	452	92	133	538	200	120	92	133	76	102	368	92

Production days next month: 20   **Factor 'z': 2.330**

	Std dev	Historical Average	Relative SD	No' of Days Safety	MPS for Next Month	Expected Production per Day	Days Lead Time	Pipeline Stock	Safety Stock	Kanban Size	Total No Kanban Tickets	Number of Red Tickets	Number of Yellow Tickets	Number of Green Tickets
	AV	AW	AX	AY	AZ	BA	BB	BC	BD	BE	BF	BG	BH	BI
PRODUCT														
Widget	47	33.4	1.4	6	900	45	3	135	255	18	22	8	7	7
Smidger	36	36.2	0.99	4	600	30	3	90	119	18	12	5	3	4
Budget	35	47.1	0.74	3	800	40	3	120	119	18	13	7	3	3
Dodger	46	56.5	0.82	3	1250	63	3	188	206	24	16	8	4	4
Seller	121	131.5	0.92	4	1850	93	3	278	344	36	17	8	4	5

MPS:	Sales forecast of 1000 – Reduction of Existing FG Stocks of 100 = **900**
Pipeline Stock:	=BB4*BA4 3 × 45 = **135**
Days Lead Time:	From personal knowledge, perhaps **3 days**
Kanban Size :	**18 Units** can be stored in each plastic 'Euro' tray
Safety Stock:	=AY4*BA4 6 × 45 = **235**
Standard Deviation	=STDDEVA(B4:AU4) = **46.8**
Total No Kanbans:	=(BC4+BD4)/BE4 270 ÷ 18 = **22**
Historical Average	=AVERAGE(B4:AU4) = **33.4**
No of Red Kanbans:	=(BB4*BA4)/BE4 (3 × 45) ÷ 18 = **8**
Relative SD:	=AV4/AW4 46.8 ÷ 33.4 = **1.40**
No Yellow Kanbans:	=(BF4-BG4)/2 (22-8) ÷ 2 = **7**
No of Days Safety:	=(S$10*AV4*SQRT(BB4))/AW4 $\dfrac{2.330 \times 46.8 \times \sqrt{3}}{33.4}$ = **6**
No Green Kanbans:	=BF4-BG4-BH4 22 – 8 – 7 = **7**
Expected Production per Day: =AZ4/K10 = **45**	

Figure 19.2. A. spreadsheet being used to calculate parameters for the design of the Widget Kanban. Note that the bottom section (columns "AV"–"BI") would follow to the right of the top section (columns "A"–"AU") if viewed on a computer. The calculations used in the spreadsheet are provided below the columns.

Chapter 20

The Kanban System in Detail

Five products—Widget, Budget, Smidger, Dodger, and Seller—were shown in Chapter 18 to be suitable for kanban control. For each of these, data has been calculated via the formulae presented in the last chapter to determine how many products any one kanban ticket will represent, and how many red, yellow, and green tickets are needed for each product.

Designing the Kanban Board and Tickets

Although it is unlikely that all five of these products would be made in the same cell, for the sake of this example we will assume that they are, and the kanban board might look like **Figure 20.1**.

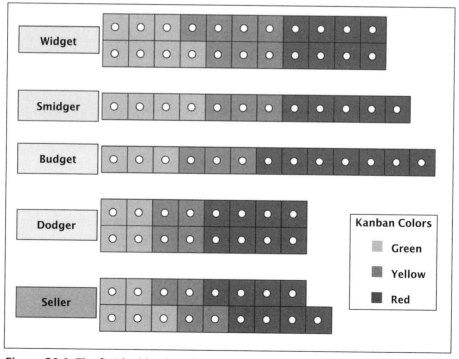

Figure 20.1. The finished kanban design.

In order to make the kanban board a reasonable size and proportion, it is recommended that, where necessary, some of the kanban patterns are two, or even three, layers deep. When you are doing this, the green portions still need to be kept over to the left, the yellow ones in the middle, and the red squares to the right.

When you have decided which products to kanban, and have calculated the appropriate number of kanban tickets for them, and have also quantified how many red, yellow, and green kanban portions each product will have, you can then start to prepare the actual kanban board. I use a free-standing whiteboard (the type used for dry-wipe marker pens). A board size of 4 feet wide by 3 feet high is best, allowing plenty of space to make the kanban tickets a reasonable size and allowing the kanban to be large enough to be visually clear, even from a distance. The white laminate gives a nice smooth background to offset the traffic light colors of the kanban. Ideally, if it can have a felt pin-board on the reverse, the same stand can also be used to show the cell's performance charts, as well as being utilized as a kanban board (**Figure 20.2**).

Before you start making up the board, I advise you to design and make the kanban tickets. Decide on the amount of information that needs to be on the ticket, such as product description, part number, quantity, and which cell the tickets belong to. Though not essential, a square ticket design makes things slightly simpler, perhaps 2 inches square. Print out your kanban tickets in the right quantities onto colored paper, then laminate them, and guillotine/cut out the individual tickets.

By using different colors, it becomes very visual which kanban tickets belong to which particular cells; this is where giving a cell a unique color identity becomes very useful.

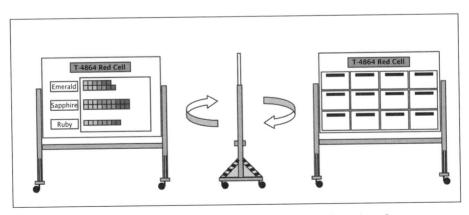

Figure 20.2. The cell notice board with a kanban on one side and performance charts on the reverse.

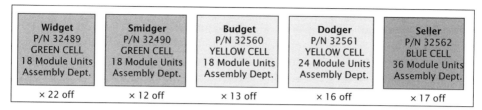

Figure 20.3. The design on the kanban tickets to go on the kanban board.

Self-adhesive Velcro (hook and loop) disc patches $^3/_4''$ in diameter are excellent for attaching the kanban tickets to the board. Of course, don't mix up the patch types. Either have all the *tickets* with "fuzz" patches and have your kanban board and kanban trays with the "hook" patches, or vice versa. Another piece of advice is to use a clear extruded clip/sleeve into which can be slid removable lengths of green, yellow, and red card. These strips are stuck to the whiteboard in horizontal rows with double-sided sticky tape. This allows you to change the kanban design quickly and effortlessly. Tickets are shown in **Figure 20.3**, and should be printed on colored paper to identify the cell (green paper for green cell, etc.).

The Rules of the Kanban Board

The kanban board is designed with the colors of a traffic light to control building product in a way similar to controlling traffic through a junction. The primary colors on the board signal which products should be stopped and which should be started. Throughout the day, the information on the kanban board changes dynamically as the cell completes trays of work and, sometime later, a downstream area consumes it. Tickets on the board represent the absence of trays of stock, tickets missing from the board therefore represent stock that is available for use. Each ticket that is absent from the board should be attached to a tray of work, held on by a Velcro patch. A tray with a ticket attached should contain the full kanban quantity that is stated on the card (e.g., 18 assembled Widget units), which is usually the number of units that will fill that particular size of container.

Ideally, the tickets should be attached to trays after the product has been fully tested and is known to be conforming to the quality standards required. However, in some circumstances, this might not be possible. An example of this would be where an overnight "soak-testing" operation has to be performed on the day's work, involving a considerable number of units. If the quantity of units being tested is significant in proportion to the potential stock represented by the kanban board, then it is sensible to attach kanban tickets to the trays even while the soak testing is in process.

Otherwise, the kanban board will not give a realistic picture of the build/demand situation.

As soon as the area downstream starts to use up units from a tray, then that kanban ticket should be removed from the tray so it can be returned to the display board. To avoid operators having to take every individual ticket back as soon as they are removed, it is wise to have them collected into a receptacle, and then once an hour a nominated person collects them and returns them to their respective kanban boards. Good housekeeping should ensure that each product line only has one partially full/partially empty tray and, therefore, that all other trays are full and carry kanban tickets.

In the build cell, the person on the final operation removes the correct ticket from the board and fixes it to the tray once it is filled. The tickets get removed from the right-hand side of the board first, to ensure that they clear out of the red, then the yellow, etc. When the nominated person in the downstream area puts the tickets back onto the board, the process is reversed, and they are loaded onto the kanban board from left to right.

The cell operators need to respond to the kanban board as it changes throughout the day. Tickets of one variety that creep into the red signals the need for the team to consider changing over production to that particular product, instead of the type they are currently working on. Tickets that drop back into the green as they are assembled and put into trays signal that the priority for that product is now low, and the team should consider building another product that is more urgently needed. I would recommend that each cell nominate a spokesperson to be responsible for deciding when these changeovers need to occur. These decision points shouldn't require a supervisor: instead, the team should feel empowered enough to make such decisions. Promoting people to be cell leaders merely adds another layer to the management structure and can be seen as divisive. However, unless one cell person is elected to say "we'll change over now," there are likely to be minor squabbles as some people won't like being told to do something unless by a supervisor.

If all the tickets on the board go into the green, the cell needs some operators to drop out in order to slow it down. The remaining people must still build as productively as possible, because they are being measured for productivity all the time. A cell whose kanban board has nearly all its tickets going into the red signals that it requires more operators. Or, if it is constrained by a bottleneck operation, it needs additional working hours. Again, adding operators to a cell to let the existing people take it easier

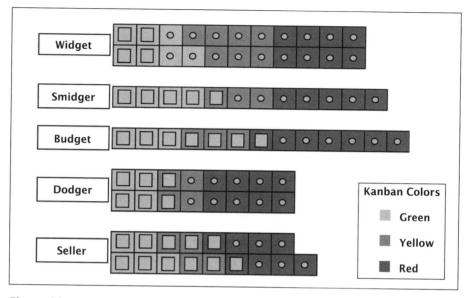

Figure 20.4. At this stage, more Sellers are produced to move more product out of the red.

can't be allowed because that productivity measure will soon signal a drop in team efficiency.

The cell, which is working to the kanban board shown in **Figure 20.4**, has just built and sent down to the kanban storage rack another tray of Widgets. It must now stop producing that variety of product and produce some Sellers. It is being manned at about the right level for the moment, and anyone can quickly (though only approximately) see how much stock of each product is being held. The cell can be confident that there is only a slight risk that the customer may not get the products they require, but it will soon reduce that risk by getting out of the red on *all* its product lines.

The Fear of Losing Control

Supervisors and managers alike are used to making the decisions and calling the shots. Several concerns will be in their minds.

1. If cells have to slow up when the kanbans are in the green, and stop altogether when all the kanban tickets have been used, what will we do with all the operators who are out of work?

This is not a reason to obstruct the implementation of kanban and pull systems. It is also not a reason to artificially manipulate the kanban by taking tickets off full trays and putting them back on the board so that the cell can continue working. A diverse product range, smooth order loading, a flexible workforce, and a flexible sales strategy are all factors that will help to avoid this scenario.

2. A manager may feel strongly that it can't be right for a cell to build product that he/she knows isn't immediately required (i.e., just replenishing kanban stocks), especially when it might be possible to tell the cell what is urgently required. This is especially a concern when the department is short of people and the manager doesn't want customer orders to miss their shipping dates.

This is a problem with any system where WIP is built. Overproduction is wasteful because it produces items that aren't immediately required. If there are sufficient operators available, then this situation won't exist and so there won't be a problem. The conflict occurs when orders increase—when several spikes in demand hit the factory and the availability of labor can't increase fast enough. This is why good sales and operations planning (S&OP) is essential, as is smoothing the loading of orders into the factory. The rest of the organization with direct links to production will need to evolve to support lean; otherwise problems and conflicts will certainly be experienced.

Dealing with the Extremes of Kanban

1. Why is one cell's kanban board always in the red?

The cell may not have enough capacity. Scrutinize the shop floor for any area where unnecessary work is being done (overproduction), and move some bodies, if necessary training them to permanently work in the cell. If it is not a labor problem, the cell has a bottleneck. Is there a piece of machinery that is acting as a constraint? If so, reduce the load on the bottleneck where possible, by taking some of the overload out of that cell and into another. Don't think it is wrong to occasionally build a product from the Red Cell in the Yellow Cell from time to time—this is all about flexibility and building the right things at the right time. If this solution isn't possible, then continuous flow may have to be compromised. Build up work in front of the bottleneck machine and get an overtime or shift worker to push it through after the cell's usual crew of operators have finished for the day. The problem could be that one or more of the products in the cell has experienced an ongoing growth in sales, and the size of the cell is no longer adequate. Add some more benches and equipment to make the cell bigger. Consider splitting the cell in two: whether it is two duplicates producing exactly the same product, or two cells each dedicated to building a specific product family where previously both product types had been built in the same cell.

2. All the kanban boards in all the cells are in the red!

Ignoring a massive material/supply issue, this is almost certainly because the shop floor doesn't have enough labor. Sometimes even a good S&OP process can fall out of step with rapid increases in demand. The quick way to hire people is to use an employment agency. The slower way to recruit is for the company to do it itself. Advertising, selection, interviewing, and offering jobs and waiting for people to serve notice periods before they start all takes time. A way of speeding up the process is to anticipate an increase in business through good sales forecasting, and to have started the recruitment process early. If the business has a healthy number of application forms on file from people that have been screened into a short list of potential interviewees, then the majority of the recruitment delay is leap-frogged.

3. All the kanban boards in all the cells are in the green!

When kanban boards are being utilized in most parts of the operation and almost all of them are in the green, you have a major problem. In this situation, the operations director needs to decide the best course of action. If a busy period is *definitely known* to be just around the corner, then the sales office could place internally generated stock-building orders on the dispatch department to build FG stocks. If the company currently has agency workers on the shop floor, then should they continue to be retained? Now the decisions get harder. Is it time to cancel overtime? Should the factory go onto just one shift or shorten its working week? This is easier if there is an annualized hours working agreement. The last resort in business would be to consider redundancies.

Chapter 21

Creating a Pull System

Once several U-shaped cells have been implemented, some kanban replenishment systems have been created, materials are stored lineside, and the supply of materials has gradually been changed to support little-and-often delivery of components, then you have probably just about arrived at an important evolutionary stage of lean—a *pull system*.

A pull system is where the whole manufacturing system is geared to responding to the demand from customers. The first part of the system to react is the dispatch department, who customize, pack, and ship orders from a small kanban stock of assembled product. The various assembly areas then replenish whatever items are removed from the kanban stocks they feed into by using a kanban board for visibility. Whatever subassemblies and components the main assembly cells consume in doing this, signals—via further kanban system cells farther upstream—what work to replenish, and so on. The result is that the customer requirements are pulled through the factory by the downstream operations right through to the upstream operations. This is totally opposite of traditional production planning where the initial operations and the subsequent ones are instructed what to do according to a complex production plan, and the dispatch end hopefully gets the right products in the right quantities before the delivery date is missed. The traditional method of operating a factory is, in contrast, called *a push system* because the work is pushed in at the front end until it pops out at the dispatch end some time later (with the help of progress chasers).

One or two cells in isolation, especially when they are "parallel" to each other rather than upstream–downstream of each other, is not a pull system, it is just a small segment of pull in a sea of pushing. It takes many months, even years, to develop the majority of the shop floor into a network of cells linked by kanbans and supported by lean purchasing.

After changing to cellular production with kanbans, lineside storage, and faxbans, there comes a point where the dispatch end becomes truly linked all

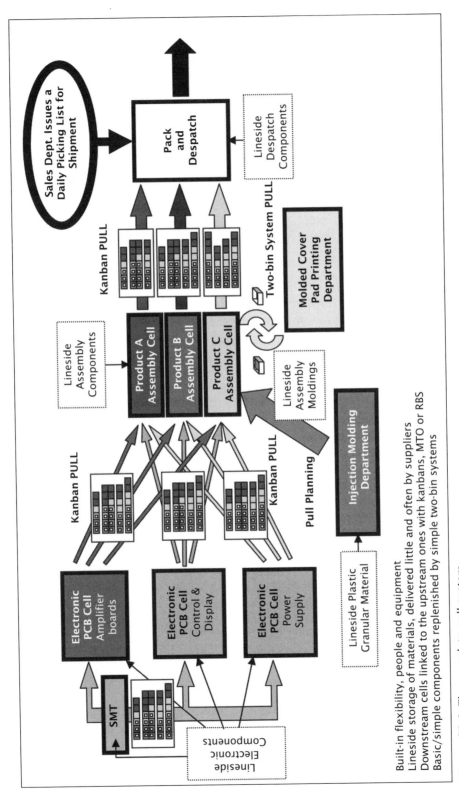

Figure 21.1. The complete pull system.

the way upstream to connect to the goods-in-door by systems that require very little supervisory intervention. Even if the first part of the production process is moderately "batchy" because it is comprised of a press shop or an injection molding shop, this might not matter. As long as it is planned according to the pattern of consumption from the cells immediately downstream, rather than being planned by a production planner, then it still counts as a continuous pull system. When you have reached this point, a significant milestone has been reached and congratulations are in order. A pull system is illustrated in **Figure 21.1**.

Attainments

- Lead time reduced from 20 to 30+ days to single figure days, i.e., between 1 and 9

- Work now flows much better, less end-of-month overtime is needed to finish off orders

- Value of inventory has been halved, mainly FG and WIP, but to some degree raw materials will also have been reduced

- Operator skills and flexibility will have greatly increased

- The culture of the shop floor is more accepting of change; there is now real ownership

- Housekeeping standards are far better, and several "visual factory" comparisons are possible

- Major quality screw-ups (the rejection of large batches) are now a thing of the past

- The shop floor no longer needs production planners or quality inspectors, and the number of storemen has been halved; and, for instance, only a small incoming goods department is now required because several suppliers now make lineside deliveries.

Chapter 22

Production Meetings

Lean production necessitates that many day-to-day activities will have to change. The running of the shop floor is clearly one of these areas. The target-driven philosophy of a push system will need to be replaced with new performance measures that are geared around each cell continuing to improve in everything it does. It will no longer make sense to look back on what happened over the last weeks and months, and compare the results to what production quantities were expected. Instead, it will become necessary to concentrate on the next few days and weeks to ensure that the necessary actions are taken to meet the changes in customer demand. The production meeting, where the daily production status reports are scrutinized, is one of the areas that will quickly need to adapt as the old push systems change into kanban driven pull systems.

Traditional Production Meetings

A traditional/conventional production meeting can, of course, take many forms. It is typical that the adherence to the targeted build rates for each product would be reviewed. Material shortages, any machinery breakdowns, and the availability of operators would also be mentioned. Finally, any customer delivery problems would be highlighted. An example of a traditional production report is shown in **Figure 22.1**: it details the progress against the monthly build targets that are commonplace in traditional push systems.

Unless very substantial finished goods stocks are held, controlling, monitoring, and reporting such data at the same time as trying to keep to a steady build plan will in no way guarantee that customer orders are satisfied. Forecasts are usually wrong, especially in predicting the product mix; and the monthly build targets are also inevitably flawed in terms of accuracy. It is therefore necessary to monitor the sales intake to see how the levels of demand for individual products compare to the forecast, and how the overall shipment/invoicing levels compare to budget. Doing this will

Production Days Passed: 11   Production Days in Month: 20   55% Time Elapsed

	Product	Variant	Expected Avg/Day	Built Yesterday	Built Month to Date	Target Month's Build	% to Target
Red Cell	Widget		40	37	367	800	83.4%
	Budget		60	70	692	1200	104.8%
	Fudgit		25	12	245	500	89.1%
Section Subtotals			**125**	**119**	**1304**	**2500**	**94.8%**
Blue Cell	Smidger	I	32.5	25	345	650	96.5%
		II	12.5	30	180	250	130.9%
		III	37.5	40	363	750	88.0%
Section Subtotals			**82.5**	**95**	**888**	**1650**	**97.9%**
Green Cell	Dodger	I	4	0	23	75	55.8%
		II	47.5	75	256	950	49.0%
		III	26	10	176	525	61.0%
	Seller	I	50	0	980	1000	178.2%
		II	150	185	1759	3000	106.6%
Section Subtotals			**277.5**	**270**	**3194**	**5550**	**104.6%**
DEPARTMENT TOTALS			**485**	**484**	**5386**	**9700**	**101.0%**

Figure 22.1. A production report sheet that is more appropriate for traditional production methods.

allow production targets to be adjusted, as and when necessary, throughout the month. All too often, there will be surprise shortages, and the need to expedite certain products through the system will occur daily.

So, in this scenario there are a lot of numbers to monitor, check, report, compare, and adjust. All this takes a lot of supervisory time and effort. The strategy of holding more FG stock to reduce the risk of failing to satisfy customer demand, and any objectives of reducing material stocks to control WIP cost, will be in conflict with one another. Whatever FG stock levels are decided upon, it will always be a decision of compromise.

There are other issues that muddy the water. If stock of some components is depleted, the decision at the production meeting will often be to build more of the products that don't require that component, in order to keep everyone busy. In extreme cases, what materials the purchasing department can or can't obtain can dictate much of the build program.

There is also a risk that the FG stock protects production from adjusting to the real trends in customer demand, and that there may be a temptation for supervisors to cherry-pick. An example of this would be for a supervisor to assemble lots of product that is particularly quick to build to make it appear that the factory is managing to keep up with the required build rate (units per day) when, in fact, it is falling behind. If productivity calculations are prevalent, it might be advantageous to build products that have been given "slacker" times. A supervisor who knows that he/she has left it too late to achieve the month's build target on one of the product lines can swamp the area with operators in the last week of the month. This will strip bare the available component stock without hope of the stock being replenished soon enough, and in this way the blame for the failure can be shifted onto the material department: they should have brought in more components, shouldn't they?

Let us now stop looking at traditional factory practices and start over again—this time with a focus on smooth work flow, freedom from waste, and continuous improvement.

A Lean Manufacturing Production Meeting

A key principle in lean manufacturing is to build only those products that there is an immediate customer demand for. As long as there is an element of demand smoothing (see the next chapter) as well as a supply chain system designed to facilitate lean, this should not be a problem. This means that, in most cases, it is possible to operate with little or no finished goods stocks, using short-range sales forecast data to prime the supply chain. Instead of organizing production around weekly or monthly build targets derived from inaccurate long-range sales forecasts, the manufacturing cells will build to kanban boards that respond directly and dynamically to real customer demand patterns. This is clearly a fundamentally different manufacturing system and represents a working style and culture entirely different from the one most people have been used to. The production reports and production meetings need to suitably reflect this.

The change in focus has to be toward:

1) compliance to the rules of the kanban boards,

2) attainment of good *but also improving* cell productivity scores,

3) critical issues that have occurred on the shop floor and corrective actions needed,

4) a macro current status compared to forecast comparison and commentary (simply to keep understanding how order demand patterns are changing compared to the S&OP), and

5) determining if adjustments can be made to both reduce lineside stock levels still further and also how recent stock-outs can be prevented from happening again.

The new style production report (see **Figure 22.2**) has information on two significant subassembly cells on the left, and information on the three final product assembly cells on the right. Each cell has its kanban board visually portrayed, together with the productivity score from the previous day. There is also some macro build information to indicate whether the demand is greater or less than that forecasted. This helps to suggest capacity adjustments. Covering all the key information in this new-style production meeting will require only 10–20 minutes.

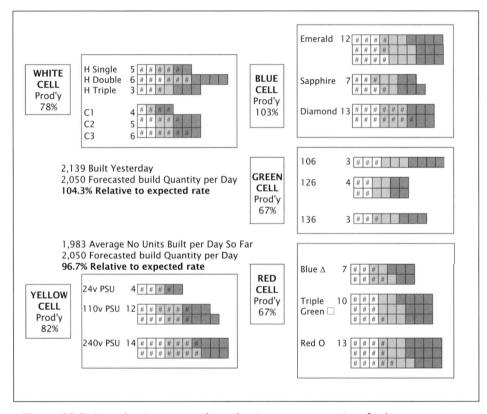

Figure 22.2. A production report sheet that is more appropriate for lean production.

Chapter 23

Support for Lean Manufacturing: Material Management

Lean purchasing is all about supporting the factory's lean cells by providing them with a supply of materials so they can flexibly build according to the changing demands of the end customer. It is an additional benefit (but NOT the principal objective) if, in the process, raw material stocks can also be reduced by some degree.

The key way that modern material purchasing can reduce raw materials stocks is by organizing little-and-often deliveries, an arrangement that is often possible only by changing the company's relationships with its vendors—including the number of vendors it deals with.

Big centralized storerooms, common in traditional factories, are no longer appropriate for modern lean manufacturers. Instead, lineside storage of components is required so that the visibility of parts and accessibility is greatly improved. By lineside, I mean that the components needed in a cell should be kept as close to the cell as possible, instead of removing them from the production area into a temporary facility because of a belief that parts need to be "controlled" efficiently. In a traditional factory, all materials have to be "managed." In a lean operation, the kanbans of WIP and the small quantities of finished goods are managed autonomously. The materials team is left to concentrate on the role of guaranteeing the supply of outside components and ensuring that the company's replenishment systems are performing as required.

Lineside Materials Storage

One of the most frustrating things a production team experiences all too often is the lack of availability of the parts it needs. The frustration is particularly great because the workers feel that they have no control over the situation, and thereby become resigned to knowing that stock-outs will occur again and again. Nobody likes to go home after a day at work knowing they have achieved very little, or haven't been very productive. Therefore, one of the biggest things that can be done for the shop floor is to dramatically improve the availability of parts and eliminate the causes of stock-outs.

Getting the cell's material located adjacent to the cell makes the components *accessible* and *visible*. The leading hands can then be given *ownership* of their own material. By labeling the racks and shelves clearly, and stipulating maximum and minimum replenishment levels, the leading hands will be more than capable of controlling these materials. In fact, the leading hand is the best person to whom this sort of routine task can be delegated, because he/she is the expert person in that department. A storeman, on the other hand, works in a completely separate department and will not have the same level of ownership and commitment to ensuring that the availability of materials is uninterrupted. Storemen will usually be working at a slower speed and to a different set of objectives and priorities. If a leading hand has to go to the storeroom with a materials request, it can often be several hours before the materials are supplied to the work area. It is possible that the workers were unable to continue working for some, or all, of this time, and this is yet another cause of a traditional factory being less productive than a lean organization.

Lineside storage necessitates good housekeeping. The locations and part numbers will need to be very obvious and clear so that operators can quickly locate the components they need. Do whatever you can with the labeling on both the shelf and the container to make it obvious if someone puts materials in the wrong location: color coding on the labels is good for this. Pay special attention to mistake-proofing separate locations for parts that are different, yet identical in appearance, especially if they are supplied in similar packaging.

Material Supply for Lean Manufacturing

Lineside material/parts quantities should be held only at the necessary levels—any greater than this means cash is unnecessarily tied up. Keeping these levels low and lean will require the delivery frequencies from suppliers to increase.

Vendor Reduction

Should a lean manufacturer have lots of different suppliers, or should it have a strategy of having a minimum number of vendors?

Advantages of having lots of vendors:

- able to switch between alternative suppliers frequently to assure that the purchase price is always as low as possible

- dual sources reduce risk of failed supply (or does it?)
- reduced cost of switching vendors (fewer items with any one supplier).

Advantages of having fewer vendors:

- more purchasing power/leverage (bigger account size)
- reduced administration costs
- more negotiating leverage for frequent deliveries.

Traditional companies will try to minimize every purchasing cost, whether that means bulk buying or selecting vendors based solely on who offers the lowest individual component cost. This leads to having numerous separate vendors, with some supplying only one component. However, each supplier requires administrative effort to maintain. If you were one of these component suppliers and you only supplied, for example, two parts, you would not be enthusiastic about making more frequent deliveries. On the other hand, if you were a vendor that supplied 40+ different components to a single customer, it would not be unreasonable to agree to commit to several dropoffs per week. You would also be more inclined to offer a more competitive price because of the overall quantity of business being done. When a manufacturing company decides to become lean, its material purchasing team needs to renegotiate terms to attain little-and-often deliveries. This process will require the company to dramatically alter its purchasing strategy, reducing its fragmented supplier network through a process of consolidation.

The process of vendor reduction allows a company to renegotiate terms with the most appropriate suppliers so that little-and-often deliveries with no increase in cost can become a reality (slight cost reductions are, in fact, often possible).

Negotiating a Better Level of Supplier Service

As WIP (raw materials are not included in the sense of this term) is reduced and removed from processes, there is more and more pressure on purchasing to be responsive to changes in demand. These changes in demand for parts will happen far quicker than before because there is now very little lag in production response to variations in customer demand. The concurrent desire for the company to reduce its levels of component holdings will mean that the possibility for the suppliers to hold some buffer stock needs to be explored. Suppliers probably already hold stock to some degree. However, if it can be agreed in writing as to how much stock of which part numbers will be held, it will more likely result in the right quantities of the right parts being held compared to leaving the supplier guessing what stocks, if any, they should hold.

A traditional company with many suppliers to play against each other can be a fickle organization with which to do business. It may change from one supplier to the next quite quickly, and this possibility is used as a veiled threat to extort the lowest component price from each vendor. Suppliers who are treated like this become very wary of such customers, and neither supplier nor customer will benefit from such an adversarial situation.

The lean organization that has selected a small number of vendors to supply broad ranges of components offers those supply companies a far more stable working relationship—one that is based on trust and partnership. This is a very valuable commodity, and it can be traded for a new price list and maybe a slight cost reduction. The selection of such preferred suppliers to consolidate purchasing is a process that should be carried out very carefully. Such vendors need to be large enough to have a regional network of localized distribution centers, one of which should be relatively close by. Ideally you should end up communicating with just one of them and be able to speak to the same contact person each time you need to get in touch. In this way, a relationship of understanding and cooperation can develop. After exploring several different potential candidates, the materials team will soon be able to decide which of the suppliers is most likely to successfully fit the bill.

Finally, and most importantly, the consolidated vendors should each have a logistical framework that can support little-and-often deliveries without any problems. Hopefully, they will be able to demonstrate that they have such relationships with some of their existing customers, and they might be willing to allow you to discuss their supply performance with these other companies.

Typical New Supply Chain Agreement Terms

A long-term agreement will be appropriate to show commitment from both sides. For example, it may be necessary to agree to a 3-year minimum preliminary business duration after which, if either party wishes to terminate the relationship, six months notice will need to be given.

Another important part of the agreement may be to provide, where appropriate, a 12-month blanket order for each different part number. For some of the high cost items, the company may need to accept liability for the cost of any residual stock—i.e., the company guarantees it will purchase the entire 12-month blanket order regardless of circumstance. By doing so, the liability for such custom materials will not rest with the supplier, who might otherwise be unable to sell the parts to anyone else. The company may also need to offer to provide a rolling 6-month forecast, issued to the supplier every month on the understanding that the first 3 months of this will be relatively fixed, and the last 3 months less so. This technique is known as "priming the supply chain," and in this way the company updates the supplier with the best information it has on the demand profiles that are likely to occur over the short to medium term.

Minor things, such as agreeing to delivery pack sizes, will also need to be negotiated, in a way similar to agreeing to the number of units that a kanban ticket should represent. The supplier will probably already have convenient minimum pack quantities, and supplying anything other than multiples of that size may be quite unnecessary and bothersome. Unless this is discussed, neither party will know what quantities are most appropriate. For a high level of service, some buffer stocks may have to be held by the supplier. What levels are required for the different components is a matter that needs to be calculated and agreed on before the relationship proceeds further.

Ongoing Relationships with Suppliers

Each consolidated vendor should be visited at least twice a year. During such a visit:

- update the supplier on changes to the business and its markets
- congratulate any successful changes since the last visit
- discuss any delivery failures
- audit the buffer stock quantities
- explore ways to improve the delivery frequency and quantity reduction
- identify additional components that can be supplied through the vendor
- consider packaging improvements to reduce damage, lower costs, or reduce environmental impact.

Replenishment Practices that Support Lean Manufacturing

Faxbans

As already discussed, the person who is most committed to ensure that the team does not run out of materials is the leading hand. The day-to-day task of material reordering is relatively simple and straightforward, so why shouldn't the responsibility for such routine material call-offs be delegated to dependable people on the shop floor? Proforma faxes can be produced so that designated supervisors can simply fill in the required information and fax the material requirements straight to the supplier. An example of such a prepared sheet might be as follows.

FAO: Jill Baker **OLDCORN STAMPINGS** Fax No: 373 2898				
Stock-check & Fax on **Monday,** Delivery Due following **Thursday**				
Quantity Required	Part Number	Agreed Maximum Holding level	Current Level	Container Quantity
500	SP-59280	1250	651	250
270	SP-59281	540	275	54
720	SP-68000	1200	483	120
648	SP-68005	900	230	36
360	SP-68006	900	525	36
From: Martin Richards **Hendridge Controls** Date: 11-8-03				

Periodically, the materials department, in conjunction with the production team, may decide to increase or decrease the agreed lineside holding levels as necessary. A system should be instituted whereby a "fresh" proforma faxban is printed each time, so that the changes to the agreed maximum holding levels are always reflected on the "current issue" faxban sent to the supplier.

Barcode Scanning

Most packages of components that are received into a factory these days have barcode labels on them as standard. The barcode simply represents an alphanumeric string of digits in a format that can be recognized by a computer. The data invariably contains the part number, which is usually also printed directly adjacent to the barcode so customers can identify the part without resorting to a computer. Barcode readers and printers capable of producing barcoded labels are commonplace and affordable these days, making it a very accessible medium. The possible application of these barcodes is that each time a pack of components is opened, the packaging has its barcode scanned immediately prior to it being discarded. Alternatively, all the used packaging is stored in a centralized cage and is scanned by a dedicated materials person each day, and only then the packaging is discarded. Several software packages are available to take this scanned data, compare it to a database of information, and then automatically contact the supplier electronically (EDI) with the replenishment requirements.

Lineside Delivery

For low cost consumable items such as nuts, bolts, springs, and washers, one wants to have a method of replenishment that adds little or no administrative burden to the organization. Many companies have specialized in offering such a service, where members of their staff come onto your shop floor each day, scan barcodes of any items that are getting low, and drop off packets of components that were scanned the previous day. Once a month, a single invoice is produced to cover all the materials that were supplied. After the initial novelty factor has worn off, this routine will become a seamless feature of the lean organization's day.

Stock Reduction

Organizing a stock reduction program across all part numbers requires a methodical approach. The priorities for stock reduction and delivery frequency increase need to be made/negotiated according to a defined strategy agreed to by the materials management team. To get quick financial benefit, it is recommended that this should start with high value, high volume items. In some circumstances, such as limited shop floor space, the physical volume that some parts take up may be a factor important enough that medium-to-high usage, large components need to be attacked first. Low value parts, even if they are used in high volumes, will likely merit different stock reduction solutions compared to high cost, medium volume components. A highly simplified example of a stock analysis is shown in **Figure 23.1**, and is discussed below.

Category A

This is where most raw material cost is tied up. It is worth spending the majority of one's efforts on reducing the quantities of these three part numbers, even if the solutions cost a little bit to put it into practice. Expensive components are often expensive because they are uniquely made to your company's requirements. Where this is the case, these items can also be expected to have long lead times when reordering. The ordering of these components should be the responsibility of a professional, such as the materials manager. If left to a shop floor supervisor, there will be a risk that the decisions about when to order and how much to order will be made without expert judgment and full consideration of business requirements. There should be no more ordered than is absolutely necessary, and the order should be placed no sooner than is absolutely necessary. It is therefore appropriate to calculate carefully how many of these special components will be needed to build the product quantities expected, as agreed in the

Part No.	Value	Annual Usage	Annual Value	Quantity Held in Stock	Stock Value
3456	$ 1.23	12,000	$14,760	1,200	$1,476
1234	$ 0.04	60,000	$2,400	4,620	$185
6789	$ 0.01	120,000	$1,200	17,150	$172
2345	$ 4.67	7,500	$35,025	840	$3,923
8910	$ 3.78	8,000	$30,240	540	$2,041
4567	$ 0.45	25,000	$11,250	2,090	$941
4321	$ 0.12	40,000	$4,800	8,000	$960
9876	$ 0.89	8,600	$7,654	720	$641
7654	$ 0.02	100,000	$2,000	6,250	$125
3210	$ 0.25	24,500	$6,125	2,450	$613
8765	$ 1.89	9,500	$17,955	640	$1,210
			$133,409		**$12,285**

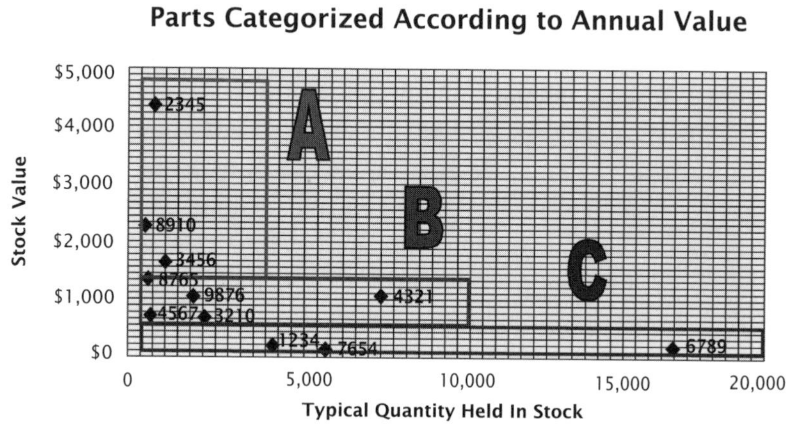

Parts Categorized According to Annual Value

	Value of Stock	% of Total Value
Category A	$7,440.00	61%
Category B	$4,363.40	36%
Category C	$481.30	4%

Figure 23.1. Categorizing material stocks in preparation for a stock reduction project.

S&OP meeting. It is also worth remembering which products use these particularly expensive specialty components, so that when demand for these products is anticipated in the sales forecast, extra effort can be paid to understanding the probability of these particular sales becoming real.

Category B

At least three of these part numbers (4321, 3210, and 4567) are good candidates for stock reduction. By attacking this category of component stock holding quantities, reasonable amounts of cash can be released, and this is therefore well worth exploring. The new systems for bringing about little-and-often deliveries should be kept relatively simple, using methods that don't require too much time or effort. Faxbans or barcode swiping could be appropriate tools. Because of the moderately high volumes used each month, there is no point in risking a stock-out by cutting the stock holding numbers down to the bone.

Category C

Here, there is a great opportunity to reduce stock quantities, but there is very little financial gain to be made in doing so. Nevertheless, unnecessary overstocking should be tackled, but any actions to achieve this for these low value items will not be worthwhile if they involve any considerable cost. In fact, it would be very worthwhile to utilize an outside "nut and bolt" supplier to come into your factory and top up these tubs on a regular basis without any administrative intervention from the company.

Summary of Lean Materials Management

1. Start improving purchasing to support lean manufacturing early. Don't wait until you find out that the shop floor cells are struggling to keep production going in the face of intermittent component supply.

2. You *can* go *too* lean. In the excitement of reducing levels of WIP, raw material is one place where you do not want to cut down the quantities held to the bone. For production flexibility, there has to be a primed level of component stock that can cope with several consecutive maximum build days. There is no such thing as an average day in production, so do not calculate stock levels using "average" consumption estimates. Hold enough to cover days where maximum quantities are being built. As finished goods, the value of product is great because labor and overheads have been incorporated, so reducing FG stock has the biggest impact. Being *overzealous* with low-value raw materials might create a situation that becomes more of a liability than a benefit. Remember, the material cost of a washer might be a fraction of a penny, but the cost of quantities of that washer *not being available* can be hundreds or thousands of dollars.

3. Clear part and location identification is extremely important. In the controlled environment of a centralized stores facility found in a

traditional factory, everything gets booked in and out of the stores in a well-ordered manner. When this is changed to lineside storage of materials, it must be crystal clear where each particular component is kept, what the part number is for each component, and what quantities are available—the latter must be conspicuously apparent. Particular attention must be paid when different components look very similar, or even identical, to one another. Avoiding situations leading to mix-ups, and the inevitable rework that is entailed, is preventive effort that is a shrewd investment.

4. Pay your suppliers promptly. In an age when companies appear to be run by accountants, it seems that not paying suppliers on time is a very easy (and fashionable) game to play to get a quick improvement in cash flow. But suppliers aren't stupid; do it once or twice and your terms of credit will be quickly cut down, and word will soon pass from one supplier to the next that your company is a bad risk. Having suppliers put your account on hold for reaching a reduced credit limit will mean that you never know if your materials will be arriving from one day to the next. It is just not worth the cost to the business in terms of disruption to production's needs and customers being let down. When you have a lean manufacturing system, you certainly can't afford to play these games because you won't be sitting on a great deal of raw material stock, and it won't take long to use it all up. Then where will you be? Up a creek and, I would suggest, without a paddle.

Chapter 24

Support for
Lean Manufacturing:
Rethinking the Sales Process

The short lead times that lean manufacturing achieves reduce the uncertainties in the production system, and this can make planning a lot easier. What the lean system is not good at is coping with feast-and-famine situations that are sometimes the norm in traditional businesses. If a manufacturer implements a lean system, but still expects a feast-and-famine order book, then there is grave cause to worry. What will the company do with everyone if it hits a quiet period and the shop floor is not allowed to build up stocks? Will redundancies be more commonplace? Should the company have changed to cells and kanbans in the first place?

A feast-and-famine order book is very often the result of an ongoing traditional relationship between salespeople and customers, where it is encouraged that orders be as large as possible. Because of the size of such orders, they naturally become more infrequent, and predicting when the next large order will be received from any customer becomes harder. Large irregular order patterns make it harder to produce a sales forecast, and this makes it harder to plan the business in terms of material availability, labor requirements, and financial budgeting. Putting effort into improving the way a business interacts with its customers, and altering the style of how it makes short term plans, can help it make enormous strides toward correcting these problems and erasing concerns over whether lean manufacturing is the right way to proceed.

Forecasting

Good planning starts with a good forecast. But everyone knows and acknowledges that there will always be errors in sales forecasts. Such errors *can be reduced*, and this will greatly assist the organization to plan effectively. Forecast improvement can be achieved by offering reduced lead times and encouraging small but frequent deliveries.

Remember that if something needs improving, it should be measured and charted. In doing this with the sales forecast data versus the actual data (known when the month is completed), one can pinpoint which products are consistently over- or underforecasted, and which product sales predictions are always highly inaccurate. Doing this will help suggest which products and which customers the sales team needs to work on in building up more reliable methods of information gathering.

Often, the overall forecast will either be over- or understated compared to actual sales, and this will hint that the levels being set are too optimistic or too conservative. As soon as forecasting accuracy begins to be measured, it will encourage the sales managers responsible for producing the forecast to improve their accuracy. For the month shown in **Figure 24.1**, a salesman might optimistically judge his forecast's accuracy using the equation 594% ÷ 6 = 99%, but the actual accuracy is 90.3%, calculated as shown in the figure.

Sales and Operations Planning

There are several very important activities that cannot be carried out unless the company's management looks far enough ahead and plans effectively. Three examples of this would be the recruitment of high-standard personnel (as opposed to lower quality, higher cost agency workers), the ordering of long lead time components, and the justification and acquisition of additional capital equipment.

Poor planning will result in valuable business opportunities being squandered. This is harmful to traditional and lean companies alike. One

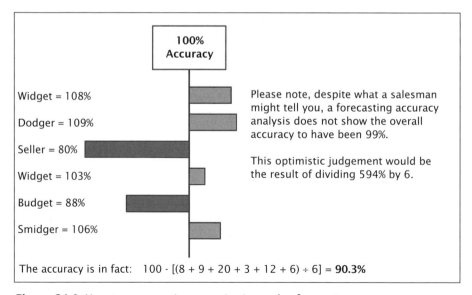

Figure 24.1. How to measure inaccuracies in a sales forecast.

might think that a lean organization is more exposed to change because it has less WIP and finished goods stock; but, in fact, it will be far more flexible and better able to react rapidly to changes in its markets. It will have selected component suppliers that can respond quickly, and it will have developed effective methods of adjusting its labor availability on relatively short notice. The traditional company may have far larger material stocks to buffer itself from change, but its component suppliers will be geared to making large monthly deliveries, and this relationship will make it awkward to get the right materials quickly into the factory when parts do run out unexpectedly. The traditional manufacturer is also likely to be more complacent about the timing of hiring people, because its stock levels dull the organization's sensitivities to the changes in demand for its products.

Companies often have a formalized sales and operations planning (S&OP) meeting each month that *should be* used as the forum to anticipate the changes happening both within the business and from outside, where plans to react to and prepare for these changes can be formulated. But it is more often the case that this opportunity is wasted, and, instead, managers prefer to spend the meeting concentrating on whether the short-term goals of hitting monthly targets and meeting budget will be achieved. Instead of looking at the three months to come, most of the meeting's time is dedicated to predicting the results and issues of the current month. Such short-termism distracts everyone from looking forward far enough, and the organization finds itself stumbling from one month to the next without a proper plan for the business.

Without a properly thought-out and adhered to S&OP process, lots of things will inevitably go wrong. The demand mix for components, compared to the actual levels of supply, gets out of balance because material purchasing decisions were made using poor quality demand information. Also, the factory is liable to find itself either over- or underresourced with people, equipment, or both.

There are several high quality inputs that need to go into an S&OP meeting to produce a quality plan. As with many things, the better the information that goes in, the better the information you will get out.

Figure 24.2 shows the key activities that are involved in good sales and operations planning. There are three distinct stages in the process. At the pre-S&OP, the input information is presented and discussed so that everyone can comment and agree on how any changes might affect the business. The second stage is to put this information into a plan—most appropriately done on a computer spreadsheet—to model how the business can best meet the demand of the coming months. The initial data that needs to be added to this computer model is the sales demand that has been forecast for the coming 3+ months. The number of production days in those months is then added, and, finally, the number of direct operators that will be available. To make the model authentic, factors such as realistic levels of productivity, sick days, and holidays also need to be added to the model. The spreadsheet will now have a realistic anticipation of the number of labor hours that will be available. By knowing the standard labor hours necessary to build each different product, and the sales demand for the coming months, the model can calculate how much labor will actually be required. By comparing the number of directs available, and the number needed for the coming months, the model thus predicts how many heads (operators) spare or heads short the factory will be.

Having put in this basic data and produced a first result, further questions now need to be asked, and then some iterative adjustments can be made to further improve the model.

Are there any stock decisions that need to be built into the plan? If it were possible, would it be best to pull some of the work forward to smooth the load on the factory? Will it be a necessary evil to build up some stocks of those products whose forecasted demand is likely to outstrip production capacity in two months time while there is spare capacity for those products in the immediate month ahead? If a new product is about to be released onto the market, what stocks of the product will need to be accumulated prior to launch?

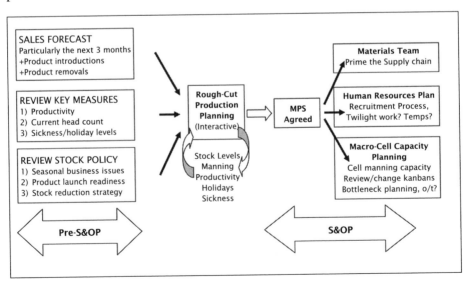

Figure 24.2. The sales and operations planning meeting, and the preparation work required.

In a lean factory, such stock policy questions will become more and more meaningless as stocks are reduced further and further, but even a lean organization may have some products that utilize rate-based scheduling, or have make-to-order products that are "bankers" to come in each month. Such products can be utilized, if deemed necessary, to soak up a slight excess of labor capacity to avoid redundancies when there is a quiet period of very short duration to be endured.

After this is done, a better comparison between the amount of labor hours required and the amount of hours available is produced, and hopefully the two will have been brought closer. Now the thought process is turned to adjusting the number by adding or reducing overtime. If the model says that you will be several heads short, the conclusion will be that you will need to hire some more workers. If this is a short-term requirement, then a boost in overtime might cover it—a medium-term requirement and a few agency workers are recommended. A long-continued requirement is better fulfilled with hiring permanent workers from an internal recruitment process.

At the other end of the spectrum, too many heads—even after taking overtime down to zero—can be counteracted by taking a step back and reconsidering some stock building. Experience and knowledge of the sales demand in the coming months needs to be used to reconsider building up stock of one or more of the products. Of course, it is best to pick a high running product that has little or no customization required to meet the needs of the customer prior to being shipped.

The leaner the organization gets, the more abhorrent any stock-building strategy will become, and the more adept it will find itself at avoiding the building of any finished goods stock at all. One highly flexible part of a lean manufacturer's toolkit, used to avoid stock building in quieter periods, is to have an annualized hours working agreement. This change in employee work contract allows the business to ask employees to work macro flex time. For example, the working week can be reduced to 4 days (e.g., 32 hours), run at $4\,^1/_2$ days (36 hours), or be raised to a full 5-day week (40 hours). Workers receive a constant weekly wage, and hours become owed by either the employee or the employer, but this is limited to negotiated levels. Either overtime is dropped entirely in return for a compensated increase in hourly rate, or overtime comes into effect once the limitations in hours owed by the company are exceeded. This type of working agreement allows yet further flexibility for the organization, but it does come with complications. Any worker trying to avoid performing additional hours needs to be identified so that the majority of people see that the rules apply to everyone. Also, the payroll/clocking system needs to be flexible enough to manage the rules.

This is an excellent way to be lean and avoid having periods where workers have insufficient work to keep them all busy. If annualized hours is a feature of the organization, then this will need to be incorporated into the S&OP model, and can be a highly useful feature for balancing capacity with demand.

An Agreed Plan

After all the iterations, a balanced business plan is produced and circulated to all parties. For the next three months it should detail:

- the expected production quantities for each product

- the expected manning levels (heads required, overtime availability).

From this, any components with long lead times can be ordered in sufficient time. All the material suppliers can be sent a forecast of component requirement patterns for the coming months, which will help them to plan their own business and greatly reduce the risk that they will be unable to supply an item in a timely manner. A recruitment plan can be generated and initiated. Finally, the team leaders, and later the shop floor, can be briefed on the levels of business and the availability/scope to work additional hours.

Reducing Administrative Lead Time

The lead time that it takes production to manufacture product from start to finish is not the only activity that has to occur for an order to result in a shipment. Prior to production commencing, orders that come into the business need to be processed, and after completion of manufacture there are shipment details to be finalized. This administrative work is often known as the sales order process.

In a traditional company, this effort can easily take up two days of the total time that the customer has to wait. In a lean enterprise, it does not make sense to have a sales order process take longer than absolutely necessary. If left unchanged, administrative work (e.g., $1\frac{1}{2}$ days) might be many times longer than the manufacturing lead time. Improving this requires the same focused effort that is employed in reducing changeover times in a press or mold shop. The first thing to do is to fully document the current sales order process, seeing what activities are really involved, how long they currently take to perform, and in what sequence they are carried out. Additionally, all waiting times and delays in the process need to be quantified.

The reasons for a traditional sales order process taking so long might be one or more of the following.

1. The system is still based on paperwork with lots of manual involvement.

2. The process is not thought of as important to perform quickly because the office staff believe that the lead time clock hasn't yet started ticking.

3. Additional steps to the procedures were added years ago for reasons that might not be relevant anymore, but nobody has bothered to remove them.

4. The way the sales office employees work follows the rules of batch mentality—they prefer to allow all the orders to build up and then deal with them all in one go, just once a day.

5. For any products that have little or no finished goods stock, the traditional company will find it necessary to request promise dates from the relevant supervisor on the shop floor. In order for the supervisor to make this judgment, it is necessary to make several WIP counts, and therefore it takes some time before a delivery date can be agreed upon.

6. A traditional company's IT infrastructure may be relatively low-tech with few printers and fewer network connections between departments. This results in administration staff wasting a lot of time walking to and from printers, and to and from departments in order to carry out their duties. It may also result in shop floor personnel having to go to and from the sales office several times a day. This all wastes valuable time.

The example of a traditional sales order process shown in **Figure 24.3** illustrates that it can easily take one and a half days to process the relevant paperwork that the order entails. Reducing this, even by half, would be a dramatic improvement.

A lean sales order process (**Figure 24.4**) will be the result of removing any steps in the process that are unnecessary and *wasteful*. Using an integrated computer system that removes much of the manual effort and paper that is generated will greatly streamline the process. In redesigning the process, mistake-proofing techniques can be built in to remove the risk of shop floor or office staff working in a nonlean way, such as the use of an order smoothing spreadsheet. Having a lean manufacturing process, where

WAIT TIME	TASK TIME	
	1 min	Customer orders arrive into the office via a fax machine and through the post. A day's orders are allowed to "batch-up" so that the sales administration staff can process all the orders in one hit.
24 hr	5 min	The orders are picked up from the fax machine and looked through. There are usually several orders that necessitate the sales office asking production when some products can be built by.
3 hr	10 min	By midday, the answers from the shop floor on delivery dates have been given. A member of the internal sales team begins the sales order process by retrieving relevant account/branch/price/product codes from Customer Terms list
10 min	4 min	Input order details onto the computer mainframe system allocating the order with a dispatch date along with all the other orders received
15 min	4 min	Print an acknowledgement to the customer and make a sales office copy
2.5 hr	2 min	Wait till 3:00 pm, then print out the day's various order breakdown sheets from the computer mainframe system
20 min	4 min	Pass printouts on to the factory
LEAD TIME		WAIT FOR GOODS TO BE PRODUCED
20 min	4 min	Team Leader separates the most recent order/shipment printouts into separate copies for the various departments, e.g., assembly, packing, and dispatch
40 min	4 min	When goods are available, the dispatch is cross-checked and the relevant dispatch sheets are stamped "Complete" and returned to the sales office
15 min	2 min	The part/full shipment information that is received by the sales office gets transferred onto the back of the copy of the order acknowledgement that sales will keep
15 min	4 min	Invoice is processed on separate computer
15 min	2 min	All invoices are printed and collected
15 min	2 min	Carton labels are printed and taken down to dispatch
15 min	2 min	Consignment note typed into computer
-	1 min	Carrier consignment note printed in dispatch
10 min	1 min	Carton labels are fixed to boxes and blue consignment note put in a wallet on one of them
-	2 min	1st copy of invoice sent to invoice address through the post
-	2 min	2nd copy of invoice sent with goods to delivery address
-	2 min	3rd copy of invoice given to accounts department to await net monthly payment

	Waiting Time	Active Task Time	Total Time
Before Production	1815 min	30 min	1845 min
Once Production is Complete	130 min	28 min	158 min
	32 hr, 25 min	**58 minutes**	**33 hr, 23 min**

Figure 24.3. A breakdown of a traditional sales order process from receipt to dispatch.

flexibility and dependability are built in eliminates the need for sales office staff to constantly query when orders can be promised.

With a pull system, production lead time can be reduced to just a few days. In this situation, the company can expect to gain sales order growth. If the administrative sales order process is also reduced, the customers will benefit

WAIT TIME	TASK TIME	
15 min	1 min	Order received manually from an existing customer. A member of the sales administration staff won't attend to the new order until they have finished their current task.
1 hr	2 min	The new order just received is added to an order smoothing spreadsheet which serves to advise when orders can be produced (in the next 1–3 days). If the lead time needs to be greater than 3 days because the factory is fully loaded, a later delivery date is shown and the customer is advised. If an order for any one product is overly large, the smoothing tool advises the sales staff to contact customer to request that the order is broken into smaller constituent parts.
4 hr average	4 min	Each hour, any orders that have come in are inputted into the NEW computer database, which already contains all relevant account/branch/price/product-code listings. The delivery dates assigned to each order are those as advised by the smoothing tool spreadsheet.
	2 min	Although the orders are now in the system, nothing is initiated by production until they receive their printouts. These are printed out at 3:00 pm each day.
20 min	10 min	Packing and dispatch are NOT given individual order prints. Instead they use their computer screens to see one order at a time for the orders to be dispatched THAT DAY ONLY. The Supervisor and packing Leading Hand are given summary sheets. The Supervisor makes daily build plans from the smoothed daily orders.
	LEAD TIME	WAIT FOR GOODS TO BE PRODUCED
20 min	4 min	When the packed goods are available, the Leading Hand in the packing area sends the dispatch details through to the dispatch room. This ensures that the dispatch person only "order picks" and prepares those orders for which every item is available.
20 min	2 min	Once dispatch person has made up the complete delivery, the packing details are typed into the dispatch computer and passed electronically to the sales office confirming what will be shipped that day.
5 min	2 min	The sales office makes a quick check that the customer's account status is ok (they have paid their last net monthly account bill on time) and the invoice process is authorized.
	4 min	The invoice documents automatically print out in the sales office and in accounts. The carton labels automatically print out in dispatch.
15 min	2 min	The dispatch person puts the labels on the boxes; an order whose labels fail to print because a <u>customer's</u> bill has not been paid cannot be shipped.

	Waiting Time	Active Task Time	Total Time
Before Production	335 min	19 min	354 min
Once Production is Complete	60 min	14 min	74 min
	6 hr, 35 min	**33 minutes**	**7 hr, 8 min**

Figure 24.4. Breakdown of the new streamlined sales order process.

even more. By applying lean principles to the sales office, the administration time can be reduced to a matter of hours.

Smoothing the Demand Load on the Lean Factory

Lean manufacturing allows the business to concentrate on the immediate sales demand. Nondisciples or the uninterested might assume that a manufacturing system now capable of short lead times will be able to cope with anything thrown at it. They would be wrong. For consistently high productivity levels and smooth small-batch manufacture with low levels of finished goods stock, *there is a very great need for spike-free factory loading.* The first step toward achieving this is to stop believing that the "customer is always right"—it is a belief that can be used as an excuse for not confronting traditional sales "habits" that do not work in a lean factory.

The Role of "Externally Facing" Sales Staff

Salesmen are used to being praised for bringing in big orders—the bigger they are, the more praise they expect. Salesmen won't have an understanding of lean, and the intuitive belief will, therefore, be that they are helping the factory to be efficient by getting them big chunks of work that will offer the economies of big-batch production. In reality, if the lean factory is asked to fill one very large order for a particular customer, all in one consignment, then it will have to starve any other customers of product (there are no finished goods to draw from). If this is a common occurrence, the factory finds itself in a feast-or-famine situation: on busy days, it will be difficult to keep up with the orders, and on quiet days it will be difficult to find work to do.

The pricing structure that most companies offer usually has price reductions or discounts at several different levels of escalating order size. In a traditional company, this is justified because everyone accepts that fewer lengthy setups and bigger batches will achieve a lower cost product than producing smaller sized orders in smaller batches. With lean production, there will be very little difference in production cost between building single-figure numbers of product and producing hundreds all in one go. In either scenario, the lean shop floor gains from the ability to produce efficiently without the wastes of overproduction and the burden of high inventory costs. Therefore, these discounts become a wasted profit margin. The only benefit they may continue to bring is to saturate the customer with *your* products, leaving no space for any of the competitor's. Volume price breaks encourage big-order mentality that really isn't healthy for any organization, whether it is the customer or the manufacturer. Profit margins are reduced for the producer, and inventory costs are increased for the customer. (Note: this discussion ignores project/contract work and new product introductions where design, tooling, and other costs are incurred. These costs will have to be recovered across the order quantity, whatever its size happens to be.)

What customer needs *all* the units supplied to them right away in one large delivery? It is very rare that they do—perhaps it happens when there is a big contract installation program. It is far more likely that customers only use the products they receive in a relatively smooth little-and-often pattern, which is why they might be encouraged to receive them that way, too.

If your company can make the number of units that the customer *really* needs at any one moment, and deliver them when they are *truly* required, then this has got to be a big competitive advantage—an advantage that may help to justify maintaining the price at its current levels when the competition are under pressure to reduce theirs. One may even be able to increase prices because of the demonstrated increase in value to the customer.

To change these habits will take time, but if it is done in a well-thought-out way and strategically planned for, then this could be one of the easiest changes to make in the evolutionary journey the organization will take to become fully lean.

First, the sales team needs to be shown what has changed on the shop floor and what it means to the organization. Next, the sales team needs to demonstrate to itself through analysis and charts that levels of customer service are higher than they have ever been, and that they can expect this to continue. Nothing makes a salesperson's job harder than when manufacturing lets the customer down and the sales rep has to make up the excuses. Inevitably, the hard won trust and confidence that they've been trying to build up with their client base is diminished. Once the sales team has compared recent performance to that prior to lean, they will have confidence that the manufacturing process has permanently improved its flexibility and reliability. Confidence about delivery performance and product quality (both of which are improved by lean operations) is a very powerful part of a sales person's bag of tools. The sales team should take this hard data with them as evidence of what levels of service can be expected when they visit customers. With some well-reasoned arguments, it can be shown that levels of service will only improve if order sizes become smaller and more frequent. Any changes to the traditional volume discounted price list will need to be agreed on and prepared beforehand. Any resistance the customer might have in going to smaller batches can only be based on losing the discounted prices—low prices that it sees as strategically more important than anything else offered.

The Role of "Internally Facing" Sales Staff

Once the orders arrive in the sales office, if the orders are loaded onto the factory according to the precepts and considerations that traditional sales office administrators think are important, then the result will almost certainly not suit lean manufacturing, and customer service levels will be put at risk.

As an example, a sales office might set itself the objective of loading orders onto the factory within the same day that they were received so that paperwork doesn't build up. This might be done irrespective of the daily order volume it generates. Apart from instances where specific delivery dates are requested, all orders are given a dispatch date in "x" many days time, where "x" is the standard lead time being promised. This seems a nice and simple rule for the sales office to work to, and it may have been fine when there were large quantities of finished goods in stock. However, a lean production system will find it hard to cope if little or no consideration is given to order smoothing. If the sales office is physically and emotionally removed from the shop floor, it won't appreciate that there are finite capacity limitations and a limitation to the elasticity of component replenishment capabilities.

The effect will be that, on some days, large quantities of work will need to be shipped—perhaps twice or three times the volume compared to the average day. Conversely, it also means that on some days hardly anything will get loaded, and "x" days later there is almost nothing to dispatch. Because of the stresses and strains this puts on a factory, this scenario is a breeding ground for late or incomplete shipments, and disappointed and dissatisfied customers. Dealing with amendments to invoices, or even having to cancel invoices, made on the assumption that they would dispatch, is an increase in administrative burden, as is telephoning the customer to explain the situation and informing them when they will get the rest of their requirement.

Once the manufacturing process is lean and isn't protected by buffer stocks of finished goods, any decisions or actions made by support operations (materials purchasing/sales processing) that are done in isolation are more often than not going to fight against the effectiveness of the organization as a whole. Lean requires the entire philosophy of the organization to be reexamined and adjusted so that it works together in harmony. With regards to the sales office, this means smoothing the orders. Where particular customers are asking for large and infrequent deliveries, those customers need to be contacted to discuss breaking the order down into two or more separate deliveries. Smoothing orders before they are loaded onto the shop floor is just as essential to working lean as is changing the material supply system to receive parts on a little-and-often basis.

Spiky Orders Loaded Onto a Lean Factory Results in Late Shipments

The top section of **Figure 24.5** shows an example of how orders are received into a sales office over the course of several weeks. The quantity of orders received on each day of the week is shown in the columns. Some days are busy, and some are quiet. The middle and lower parts of the figure show two slightly different outcomes of not smoothing the work—ways in which a lean production system with no finished goods stock could build

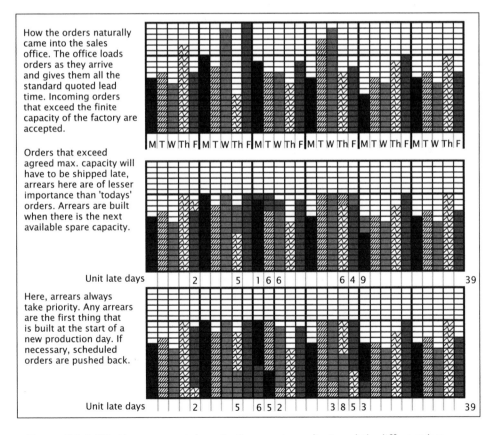

Figure 24.5. Whether arrears take priority or not results in subtly different late shipments.

the work when it has a finite number of operators and therefore a finite build capacity.

Whether orders that are in arrears are given precedence, or original orders are deemed to be more important, the total number of "unit late days" is still the same, and the damage caused to customer relations is equally bad. The point is well made: without FG stock and with little WIP, there is no buffering and the factory is very exposed to the disruption that spiky orders cause. Over the course of the six weeks shown in the example there is a total order book of 362 units; of these, there were 39 unit late days, a complete and on-time delivery rate of 89%. This is not very satisfactory.

The Effect of Smoothing the Order Loading Onto the Lean Factory

If the orders are smoothed, the customers will be receiving more achievable and realistic delivery dates. During the smoothing process, the options are either to think about bringing orders forward or perhaps pushing the delivery date back by a day or so. Where appropriate, the sales team can choose to talk to customers about whether large single orders can be split into smaller parts and delivered separately. Like balancing a one-piece-flow cell, the smaller the constituent parts, the easier the smoothing process will be (**Figure 24.6**).

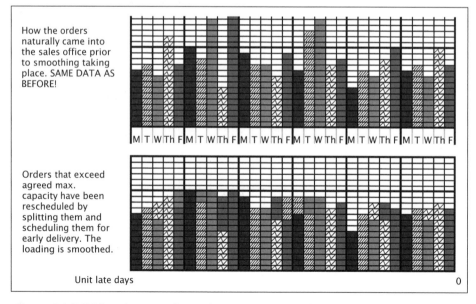

Figure 24.6. With order smoothing, the same pattern of orders can now be delivered on time.

It is now a definite possibility that none of the orders will be late or incomplete. Also, the customer is gradually being educated that this supplier 1) can deliver reliably, and 2) can offer shorter-than-industry-quoted lead times. The customer, sooner or later, will acknowledge that large single orders were indeed inconvenient. Not only will a strong partnership grow on this basis, but also any alternative suppliers who still occasionally deliver late and can't match the short lead times will eventually lose business to the lean supplier.

Smoothing in Practice

The rules of smoothing can be as simple or as complicated as you like. In my mind, though, the simpler it is, the better it is. The basic rule could be that the sales office cannot load more than 125% of the forecasted daily

Data for Next Week PRE-SMOOTHED

Product	Forecasted Daily Rate	Cell Product-Family Average Build Rate	Maximum Rate = 150%	Mon		Tue		Wed		Thu		Fri	
Emerald	121			132		168		97		189		145	
Sapphire	65	264	396	34	**255**	85	**351**	45	**277**	67	**380**	45	**222**
Diamond	78			89		98		135		124		32	
106	30			34		0		22		55		45	
126	35	88	132	23	**102**	67	**112**	45	**105**	68	**157**	32	**89**
136	23			45		45		38		34		12	
Blue Triangle	67			54		120		23		87		89	
Triple Green Circle	89	299	448.5	100	**234**	150	**470**	0	**177**	0	**297**	250	**378**
Red Circle	143			80		200		154		210		39	
Average Total:	**651**	**977**		**591**		**933**		**559**		**834**		**689**	

MAX TOTAL LOAD (120% x Average Total) = **782**

Data for Next Week AFTER SMOOTHING

Product	Forecasted Daily Rate	Cell Product-Family Average Build Rate	Maximum Rate = 150%	Mon		Tue		Wed		Thu		Fri	
Emerald	121			132		168		177		109		145	
Sapphire	65	264	396	34	**255**	85	**351**	45	**357**	67	**300**	45	**222**
Diamond	78			89		98		135		124		32	
106	30			34		0		22		55		45	
126	35	88	132	53	**132**	67	**112**	45	**105**	38	**127**	32	**89**
136	23			45		45		38		34		12	
Blue Triangle	67			54		120		23		87		89	
Triple Green Circle	89	299	448.5	100	**389**	150	**315**	0	**177**	0	**297**	250	**378**
Red Circle	143			235		45		154		210		39	
Average Total:	**651**	**977**		**776**		**778**		**639**		**724**		**689**	

155off   Red Circles moved from Tuesday by one day to Monday
30off   '126' moved from Thursday to Monday
80off   Emeralds moved from Thursday to Wednesday

Figure 24.7. How an order smoothing tool works.

average number of product units on any one day. Unfortunately, if this requirement was all for the same product, then the one cell producing it all would be totally overloaded and others would have nothing to do. Alternatively, the rule could be that the sales office must not load any one product at more than 150% of the forecasted daily average on any one day. But if every product was loaded in this way, you might have an overall load on the factory that was unachievable because there wouldn't be enough people.

Also, the more labor-intensive products might only be able to take on a maximum of 120% of the average day's loading, while quick-to-build products might be given looser limitations, say, a maximum of 180% of the average daily build expected. These are just a few of the many reasons that each manufacturer will need to tailor the rules for smooth loading according to their own particular needs. Some way of balancing the load on each individual product, as well as the total loading of the entire product mix, is needed.

Figure 24.7 shows an example of how the smoothing process can be practically achieved. Two criteria have been specified—one micro and one macro. First, no one family of products can be loaded at more than 150% of the forecasted average rate. The assumption with this example is that all the products shown do not have extreme variations in labor content; if this was a factor, then different micro constraints could be used. Second, the overall number of units that can be loaded should not exceed more than 120% of the total product range forecasted average (120% × 651 = 782 units). Using "conditional formatting" within the spreadsheet, if either of these limitations is exceeded, then the relevant cell is highlighted. A process of experimentally solving the overbuild issues is then undertaken until all the spikes are resolved. Notes of what was done to effect the smoothing are found under the second table in the figure.

Chapter 25

Becoming Even Leaner

The Progression from Pull, back to Push

Kanbans are attractive because they are a modern way of progressing toward a leaner factory. By using them throughout the whole process, they will help get the lead time down from one or more months (when using traditional big batch push systems) to a just few days. This massively increases responsiveness and "lean health." Kanbans also give a high degree of autonomy to the cell teams and they help change the culture of the shop floor. Operators will begin to accept small-batch production, being responsible for their own output, and becoming more and more flexible in their working practices.

When comparing the two methods contrasted in **Figure 25.1**, one of the biggest differences is the elimination of the need for a centralized production planning department. Once the majority of the shop floor has been transformed into a pull system, the materials and sales teams have been reorganized to closely support lean, and the culture of the organization has become more aligned to lean thinking, it is time for the next stage.

Kanbans are still piles of WIP, and WIP is waste. They are, therefore, a compromise to puritanical lean ethics. This means that when the organization decides to become even leaner, it may find that it is necessary to remove kanbans from the process. The pursuit of waste removal must continue to be explored until it seems you can go no further. This is the level of commitment you need to have when you are a true lean disciple.

It is possible to progress further by removing the kanbans that link each successive cell (**Figure 25.2**). If the most upstream cell, Cell A, is instructed exactly how many subassemblies of each type to build, then Cells B and C can only produce units in the quantity that they are fed from Cell A. In the early days, doing this would probably result in the B and C cells running at a greatly reduced productivity because they would be waiting for work. If the culture is right, the operators will be both able and willing

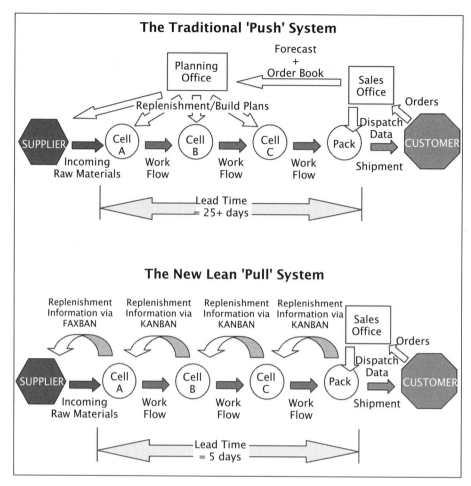

Figure 25.1. A traditional "push" system (top) contrasted to a lean "pull" system that uses kanbans to cut lead time to a few days (bottom).

to move upstream and downstream as required, so that there is little or no loss of efficiency. In this new style of push system, Cells B and C will simply require some brief information on how the units need to be customized on that particular day. The link between the sales office and packing remains unchanged.

Without the kanban WIP, the lead time will shrink to just a few hours. Making this transition involves moving successive U-shaped cells together, close enough that work can be handed from one to the other. Spaced this close, there is no longer room to store the kanban, but, more importantly, there is no need for it. This next step in manufacturing leanness means that it reverts back into a push system, but a push system that will now only take hours to completely build the products it has been instructed to generate.

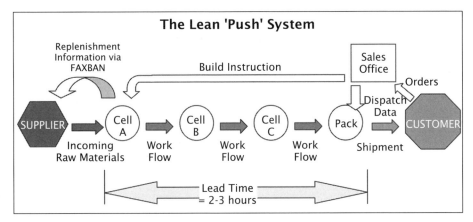

Figure 25.2. A lean "push" system can take lead time down to a few hours.

Do not think that the primary or even secondary objective of doing this is to save space—*it is not*. This is a common misconception among those who are not lean disciples. The primary objective of making this additional layout change is to get the lead time down from single-figure days to single-figure hours. The closer the manufacturing lead time gets to the value-add time, the leaner and more competitive the organization will be.

Why Not Take a Shortcut?

If the ultimate process is a push system, why is it necessary to bother creating a pull system with kanbans and U-shaped cells that will take so many months to achieve? Surely, the clever thing to do would be to go straight to the modern push system, if that is the ultimate in leanness, and avoid what sounds like a large amount of wasted time, effort, and money.

To see this as being a successful alternative will be akin to grasping at a mirage. It would be like trying to run before you could even walk. Moving benches around can be done in a matter of days. But—think for a moment—how long it will take to restructure:

- purchasing relationships and agreements with suppliers

- material location infrastructure and all the replenishment systems

- the quality system to achieve a trusted level of operator responsibility

- the sales order processing system

- the production planning structure

- the skills, cooperation, team-working, and flexibility across the entire shop floor.

Oh, and don't forget the cultural learning curve that the organization needs to go through, and the reeducation of managers away from intuitively "correct" assumptions about manufacturing, so that the changes are permanently successful and no one gives up at the first sign of difficulty.

Finally, how valuable is it to the business that it maintains its levels of customer service and stays in a situation where hard won clients are not lost? How valuable is it to retain the company's image and reputation? How valuable is it to the company's employees that they stay employed? The risks are enormous, the probability of success microscopic. It is simply a suggestive thought about taking an enticing shortcut, but it is not worth entertaining.

The journey has to be cell by cell, kanban by kanban, supply agreement by supply agreement. Wait until you have achieved "build-one, test-one" and it has bedded in. Wait until you have sufficient workforce skills and flexibility, and operators have learned to function as teams. Wait until good housekeeping is a matter of course. Wait until the manufacturing processes have had flexibility designed into them from root to branch. Wait until you have many months of proven reliability and flexibility from both internal and external suppliers. Wait until the key capacity constraining bottlenecks are so well known and understood that the sales order processing routinely plans the workload on the factory in an achievable and smoothed fashion. *Only then will you be ready to go further.*

Super Cells

A super cell is my name for what is produced when several successive U-shaped cells are combined. In the early part of the lean journey, it was best to keep U-shaped cells small, designed to contain between 3 and 6 people. This allowed a tight-knit team to form, and limited the amount of cross training necessary for everyone to start functioning together seamlessly. This allowed the team the ability to chase the work around the cell, thus keeping it flowing. Now, by moving the benches closer together, a cell is created that is three or four times the "recommended" size. But the operators are now used to cellular working, so the change is not half as revolutionary and distressing to everyone concerned as was the change from the functional layout to the U-shaped cells. The assembly methods and equipment stay largely the same as before, so neither does it represent a technically difficult metamorphosis to make (**Figure 25.3**).

How you choose to combine several cells is up to you—the permutations are great and your own particular manufacturing system is unique. The main difference now is that the work is pushed through from the initial parts of the super cell, and the downstream assembly benches have to customize whatever work is pushed their way into the product mix as required (**Figure 25.4**).

The work has no kanban trays to languish in now. Once it starts being processed, it flows through the super cell in a rapid, urgent manner. Whatever final layout is used, the super cell will need the same amounts of capacity built into it that its constituent U-shaped cells had before, especially toward the tail end where products are finished and packed. Do not expect to be able to avoid requiring anything but the same number of benches in the transformation, and expect only to save a fraction of floor space (that which used to hold kanban stock).

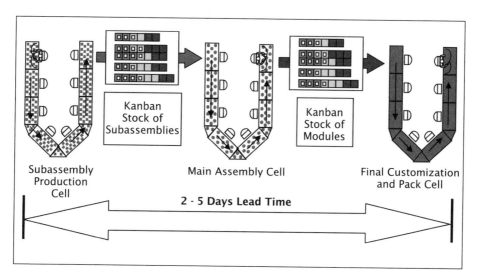

Figure 25.3. An example of how several cells can be linked together.

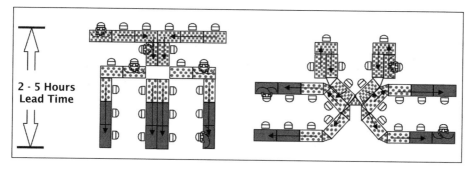

Figure 25.4. How the three cells shown in Figure 25.3 can be combined into a push "super" cell.

The two major before-and-after improvements that will be realized are 1) lead time reduction, perhaps by a factor 10; and 2) further improvements in quality. In the super cell, operators who previously worked only on assembling the final product now benefit from occasionally building the subassemblies that were previously built in a separate cell, halfway down the other end of the factory. This means that the team members make another leap forward in understanding their product's design and functionality.

Refer to **Figures 25.3** and **25.4** and imagine that six different products are bring made, here simply identified as A, B, C, D, E, and F. Now let's consider how the work can best be carried out in a super cell.

The new super cell now has the potential to build several of the subassemblies at the same time. The original Subassembly Cell building to a kanban board would only have built one type of subassembly at a time, whether it was, for example, pcb variant A, B, C, D, E, or F. Once the kanban stock for that subassembly type had been addressed, a changeover would have happened and the next most urgent of the six subassemblies would have been built. Now, the Subassembly Cell has been coupled into the super cell, it is likely that benches for these jobs will be better arranged if split into two halves. If this is done, what was once the Subassembly Cell can now build two different pcb variants at once. This reduces the transfer batch sizes, aiding flexibility and better work flow.

Much of the super cell's operations were split into small fragments of work to help operational balancing when the U-shaped cells were created. If the super cell is designed with two approximately symmetrical halves, they need to roughly share the number of "runner" and "stranger" products and have an equal share of daily work volume. If there are too many strangers on one side, it will suffer with a disproportionate number of changeovers and a disproportionately greater variety of components, jigs, and tooling. Of course, products that utilize the same test equipment have to be kept together, so a perfect balance is usually impossible. After the redesign, imagine that the A, B, and C assemblies now only flow down the left-hand side of the super cell, and the D, E, and F assemblies flow down the right-hand side. This simplification can be a great help to the team rather than trying to design a bench able to build any/every type of product.

The Rules of Push in a Super Cell

The benches at the very beginning of the process, i.e., the subassembly benches, are instructed to build a specific number of pcb variants today—for example, 132 of A, 19 of B, and 5 of C for the left-hand side, and 87 of D, 24 of E, and 2 of F down the right-hand side. A, B, D, and E are the "runners," and C and F are the "strangers." These instructions can be given to the subassembly benches quite simply by writing the details on a whiteboard kept at that end of the super cell. The whiteboard can be reclaimed from one of the redundant kanban boards, and the reverse pinboard side can still be used for performance charts.

If the subassembly benches are given the full job list describing the mix of subassemblies required for the whole day, the temptation will be for the operators to produce all 132 A's in one hit, before starting on the B's or C's. If this happens, the downstream benches get starved of B's and C's for the majority of the time. Another temptation will be for everyone in the entire super cell to concentrate on getting all the pcb variants produced quickly, in the first few hours of the day, so they can then finish the final assembly work at the tail end of the super cell in the afternoon. This, too, will result in poor work flow, and downstream benches will experience feast-and-famine in which case, by the end of the day, only two-thirds of the planned work will have been completed and the team will have achieved, at best, only a mediocre productivity score.

To avoid this, try breaking the pcb variants build instructions for the whole day into two or four separate parts, spacing them equally throughout the day. This will help steer the operators away from big-batch cherry picking and toward breaking up the work into small transfer batches that promote good flow. It will also prevent log jamming, where a concentration of one type of work hits a bottleneck operation all at once, even though the bottleneck machine had been left idle for much of the start of the day.

The following is an example of build instruction required:

		8:00 – Break	10:30 – Lunch	Lunch – 3:30	3:30 – End
Made Down Left-Hand Side of Super Cell	Product A	33	33	33	33
	Product B	10		9	
	Product C		5		
Made Down Right-Hand Side of Super Cell	Product D	23	22	22	22
	Product E	8		8	8
	Product F		2		

The operators in the super cell will by now have a good understanding that when they have finished their current work, they must move downstream to help keep it flowing. If downstream operators find themselves starved of work, they will need to move upstream to the point at which the work has built up, in order to get the work flowing again. Only by doing this will their productivity score be maintained at a high level.

The downstream operators now need to know, when they receive the pcb variants, what specific types of completed product will need to be made from them. At the middle and tail-end of the supercell, the entire day's build instruction can be stated in full, detailing all the customization required. Again, this information is written on a whiteboard for everyone to see, rather than on a printed-out sheet of paper. The middle and end of the super cell can only work with the subassembly mix of product that comes through to them. So if the pace of the pcb assembly benches is smooth and controlled, the pace of the downstream main assembly benches will be, too.

Ways to Help a Super Cell Work

The supervisor/team leader writing up the build program each day on the whiteboards should roughly know the capacity of the cell so it can be manned with the correct number of operators for the level of work to be performed that day. Given that the sales office is now smoothing the loading on the shop floor, it is likely that each day will require a similar number of operators, varying by only one or two persons each day. If the super cell is overloaded with people, it will result in a poor productivity score, and if undermanned it will fall into arrears, the day's program being impossible to complete.

It should be emphasized that operators, more than ever before, need to understand the critical importance of work flow. In traditional factories, the important thing seemed to be to maximize the efficiency at every stage by keeping operators busy with whatever work was at hand. If the correct coaching and management is not received, this intuitive reasoning could take over again in the super cell. A physical way to discourage large transfer batches would be to replace the standard size work trays with a reduced number of smaller ones.

When the middle and end assembly benches are given their customization list, the leading hand needs to check the availability of materials held lineside, such as labels and printed moldings. If any shortages can be found early on, they can quickly be replenished before a stock-out occurs.

When the different cells are combined, don't attempt to cross-train everyone immediately on all the jobs they have yet to perform. This is a medium- to long-term goal, and unless such training is done little by little the situation can get out of control, with everyone trying to train at once. Productivity would then slump to very low levels and the team would become demoralized.

With any one operator doing a greater number of tasks, and handling a larger variety of components than ever before, it will become even more important to have a "visual factory." Operators and leading hands alike will need the build instructions for each operation to be very visible and very accessible, and flip charts at their benches are ideal. Also, component and subassembly identification will need to be very visual and accessible. Material display boards that identify the ranges of components used and their respective part numbers should be created and, where possible, these boards should also display where and in which products they are used.

Chapter 26

Concluding Advice on Lean Manufacturing

In the battle for market share, the survivors who are still around in twenty years will be the manufacturers who became lean. The biggest winners will be the ones who were the first to succeed in doing so. Being happy to simply talk about changing some day, or claiming to be lean without having changed anything, is an extremely naïve game to play. In standing still, you are actually being left behind. For many manufacturers, the wake-up call only happens when they hit a business-threatening crisis that forces them to dramatically change or risk closure. In a more relaxed and stable marketplace, complacency and resistance to change make the sustained effort to become lean far more difficult, and therefore its chances for success far less likely.

Lean is a vision of perfect waste-free manufacture. To travel the lean journey will require scores of changes in every part of the operation. Initially, change will be met with considerable, albeit surmountable, grumblings of resistance. Several years into the journey, change will have become normal and expected. The popularity of resisting change gets replaced with a preference for getting involved in reshaping the organization.

One thing required to succeed in becoming lean is the empowerment and determination of key individuals in the right positions within the organization to make it happen. If these people are given the right objectives by an enlightened management team, then the required changes can happen. The directors must have the trust, faith, and confidence that lean is the right thing to do. The lean disciples must feel sufficiently trained and empowered so that they don't make the fatal mistake of feeling that there is a need to look for consensus before taking action. For the rest of the individuals in the management structure who do not become lean disciples, it is inevitable that many of them will simply not be able to shake off their long-held intuitive beliefs. They won't understand that there is anything wrong with the current practices and, therefore, they won't see why change is necessary. Get the right agents of change (the lean disciples) in place, and in sufficient numbers, and the resistance will be reduced and overcome.

Operators can be carried along with the program of lean change if they are treated with consideration and respect. Removing their frustrations cannot fail to visibly improve their performance and enthusiasm. By wasting less time having to rework rejects, and doing fewer unnecessary tasks, they will not be working any harder, they will simply be working smarter. A very satisfying aspect of the change process is seeing shop floor operators feeling triumphant and proud of the improvements they have helped make.

With knowledge and understanding of the different stages of the lean journey, it is now clear what preliminary work needs to be done, and the milestones to pass along the way. The first steps are to implement some simple replenishment systems, followed by a program of training games and setup reduction workshops, and then to take steps to have most products tested immediately after they've been assembled. The milestones that will have to be reached include the first build-one-test-one work stations, and the first U-shaped cells; completing some batch size and stock reduction programs; having kanbans instead of monthly production quotas; and rationalizing the supplier base in order to achieve reliable, little-and-often component deliveries. With orders smoothly loaded onto the shop floor, a truly visual factory emerges, and a super cell can be created that pushes product through to completion in just a couple of hours. The journey has reached its first destinations, and the company can claim to be lean.

Of course, the journey will never end, but don't worry about that. Just take the first steps and keep moving forward. Don't be unduly daunted by the scale of the changes that you now realize are necessary. All you have to do is eat the elephant one bite at a time!

Lean Training Games

A key part of making the lean transformation a success is education and training. How can people be expected to endorse lean techniques if they do not understand the principles on which these ideas are based? A set of training events will most certainly be needed to encourage people to start questioning the way things are presently done, and to relearn the benefits of working together in teams.

Ball Passing Game

Equipment
One children's half-size lightweight soccer ball

Method
This is a very simple but thought-provoking exercise for five or six people. The team is challenged to pass the ball between every individual in a predetermined sequence as quickly as they can for ten repetitions, touching the ball with their hands only. An additional rule is that no more than two people can touch the ball at any one time. If the total number of people attending the training is ten or more, split them into groups, and challenge them to beat the other team's optimum time.

Give each person in the group a number and explain that the ball will have to be passed in correct ascending numbered sequence from person to person, and the last person has to pass it back to person number one to keep the game going. Now arrange the team members haphazardly in an inward facing circle (see **Figure 1**). Because the circle is large and the ball's motion is so chaotic, the ball is likely to be dropped, wasting extra time as it has to be regathered. Using a small, light ball will avoid anything in the room getting broken or anyone getting hurt; but the faster the team tries to pass the ball in this first scenario, the greater the likelihood for mishaps.

Record how long it takes for the ball to be passed in the correct 1-to-5 sequence, ten times, then ask the team to discuss how the operation can be speeded up. The first suggestion will be to put the circle in the ascending numbered sequence and to bring everyone closer (**Figure 2**). Give them a chance to practice and then time them again.

Give them another chance at getting it even faster by asking them to think of something totally different; challenge them to think laterally by saying that the record speed it can be done in is 5 seconds.

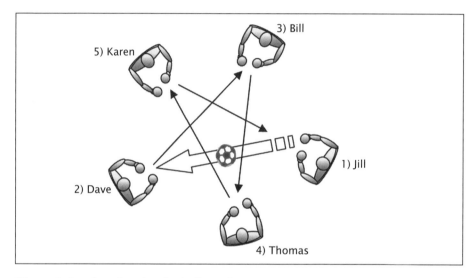

Figure 1. Starting situation for ball passing game.

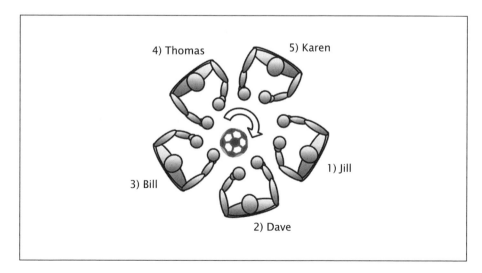

Figure 2. Second stage of ball passing game.

A good alternative suggestion is that the number 1 person should drop the ball through a vertical "tunnel" made up of the other team member's hands. The hands that form the tunnel merely brush against the ball as it drops through (Figure 3). This uses gravity to help the rapid transit of the ball. The ball is caught at the bottom by person number 1 and passed through the tunnel for nine more cycles.

The distance travelled by the ball has been reduced, and with a little practice there will be fewer chances for mistakes (i.e., a dropped ball).

If enough challenging thought is put into the game, the team might start thinking really laterally. The rules say nothing about the ball having to

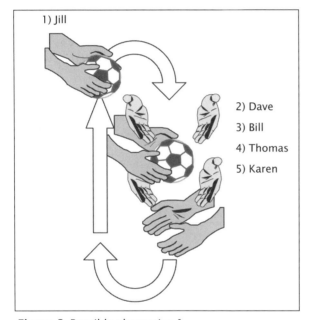

Figure 3. Possible alternative 1.

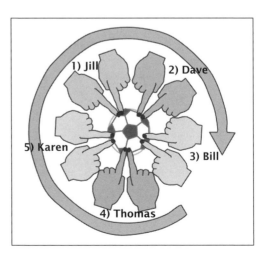

Figure 4. Possible alternative method 2.

move. Why not have the ball stationary on a table and the team gather around it and just touch it in turn very quickly but lightly with their index fingers (**Figure 4**)?

If the team does not reach this solution after four attempts at novel ways of making the game leaner, then the trainer should take the team to this solution by questioning the rules and the degree to which any motion can be minimized.

Conclusion

A solution where the workpiece is not moved and the tools only have to move millimeters is a very lean process. Yet there is an even faster solution, one that does indeed take only about 5–6 seconds. It is not described here because that would remove some of the mystery about the ultimate lean solution to this challenge. The game encourages the team to question conventional thought and to experiment with different solutions, even if some of these alternatives fail. It is good for the team to see that a process that initially takes 20–30 seconds to perform can be streamlined to such a degree that it can be accomplished in single-figure seconds.

Golf Ball Game

Equipment

60+ golf balls (cheap old lake balls, not expensive new ones)

15 half-dozen egg boxes with the tops removed

Five stopwatches

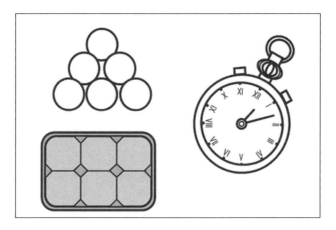

Figure 5. Equipment needed for golf ball game.

Method

This game is best played with ten people. Half of these will be timekeepers, and the other half will be operators in a pretend golf ball factory. The timekeepers use a stopwatch to prompt their "buddy" operator when to move their golf ball being "processed." The containers this pretend factory uses to move product along in are trays made from the bottom portions of egg boxes. Therefore, each container can store up to a maximum of six golf balls. There is one operator and one timekeeper assigned to each of the five different operations:

Operation 1   Mold   = 6 sec.

Operation 2   Inspect   = 4 sec.

Operation 3   Paint   = 10 sec.

Operation 4   Inspect   = 4 sec.

Operation 5   Pack   = 8 sec.

The production line is started with no golf balls in progress. The first timer says "go" every 6 seconds, at which point the first operator ("Jill" in **Figure 6**) can take a golf ball from the ice cream tub and put it in her egg box. On the sixth "go," when the sixth ball is put in the egg box making it full, she can move it from her molding operation along to Dave in the inspection operation. At the same moment, Jill takes the next empty egg box and when her buddy timekeeper says the next "go," she puts the next golf ball in, and so on. As soon as Dave has his first full egg box of molded balls, his buddy timekeeper starts saying "now" every 4 seconds, signaling the points at which he can transfer one ball at a time, from the box handed to hime by Jill, into his initially empty inspected egg box. And so the first round of the game should continue until 4 minutes has elapsed.

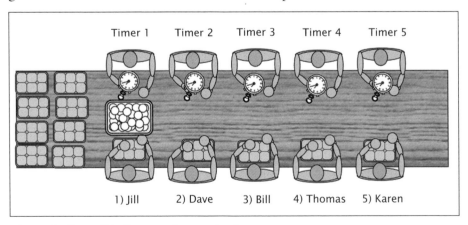

Figure 6. The golf ball game about to begin.

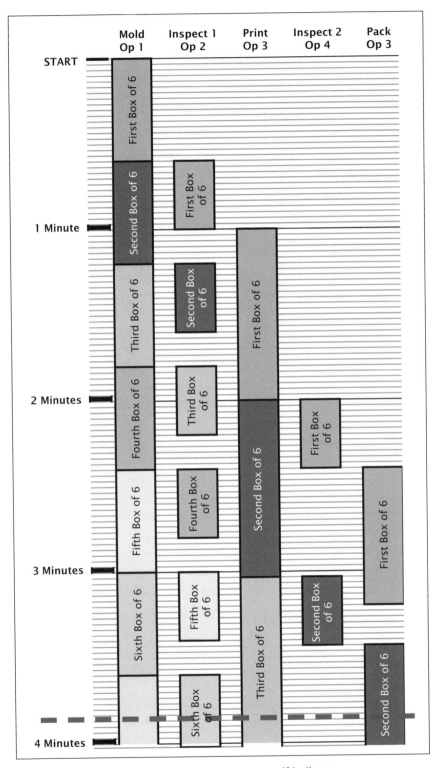

Figure 7. Diagram showing batch progress during golf ball game.

After four minutes, only one box of golf balls will have been completed. The lead time is ~194 seconds. This can be demonstrated in the game by slipping a specially marked ball into the second egg box. If this is done with any later egg boxes, it will not appear before the 4-minute game is over. The overall lead time is when it emerges from the end of the process.

After 4 minutes, the game is stopped. Enough time will have elapsed to see (**Figures 7** and **8**) that the third operation—printing—is acting as a bottleneck. This is evident because it is the only operation in front of which there is a buildup of golf balls. Dave is having to wait periodically for work to come to him, and when Thomas does eventually get into the game he is having to wait for two-thirds of the time for work to reach him. Another observation to be made is that it takes approximately 2.5 minutes for Karen to receive her first box of work.

In some further rounds, try the following, making a note of the results.

Round 2: Allow only a maximum of three golf balls to be put in any one egg box.

Round 3: Allow only one golf ball to be put in an egg box before it is passed along.

Round 4: Stay with just one golf ball per egg box, but only allow the box to be moved along if the following operation has just moved on a box leaving it with no golf balls.

Conclusion

The results from these explorations into batch theory prove beyond doubt that allowing a buildup of WIP does not get more product out the door,

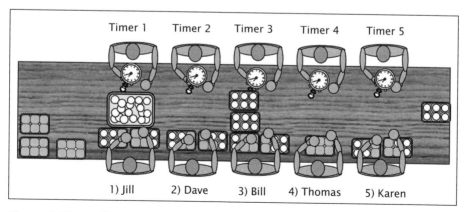

Figure 8. The golf ball game in progress (at point shown by the dashed line in the preceding figure).

or get it out any faster, instead it results in some very negative effects. The bigger the queues of work, the longer the lead time and the larger the inventory. The lead time with one-piece flow is the sum of the operational times, i.e., 32 seconds. The productivity of the system could be improved by 36% if operations 1 and 2 were combined, and operations 4 and 5 were combined. If this is done, three operators can produce 5 golf balls every minute compared to five operators producing 6 golf balls every minute.

Bristle Block (or Sticklebrick) Game

Equipment
Note: These construction toys for children are sold under the name "bristle blocks" in the U.S.A., and in the U.K. they are known as "sticklebricks."

A large tub of "bristle blocks" of various colors and designs

A laminated sheet to act as a table cover in the final round (same size as a tabletop)

Seven small square/short tables with a matching number of chairs

Several multicolored dry-wipe marker pens, one permanent marker pen

One large whiteboard (for score keeping) or a 6 foot × 3 foot sheet of paper

One flipchart (for improvement suggestions)

One stopwatch

Method
This training game teaches so much about lean manufacture that once a company finds out about it, it usually decides that all its employees must participate. It revolves around the assembly of a bristle block product—bristle blocks being a well-known children's toy. The manufacture of this bristle block product begins with a traditionally designed production system. Gradually, through participant improvement suggestions, the operation gets more and more lean. The financial success of the organization is measured after each round of the game, with the challenge being to take a disastrous, loss-making company, and make it more efficient until it becomes profitable and starts being reliable to its long suffering customer.

In the same way that a hair comb has teeth, bristle blocks have comb-like points coming out of every surface and edge; so when two bricks are pushed against each other, they stick together. Bristle blocks are an ideal medium for this game because the design of their comb-like points is such that it is very easy to make minor mistakes when trying to construct a series of products that are supposed to look identical. The assembly complications are due to two factors. First, opposite surfaces and edges have different numbers of teeth, one will have an odd number, and the corresponding opposite surface/edge will have an even number. This means that the bricks are not rotationally symmetrical, and they also have slightly different top and bottom surfaces. Second, due to the large number of teeth along each edge and surface, minor translational errors in construction can be made, making it easy for newcomers to fail to make successive assemblies identical. Without appreciating this, it is very easy to position the bristle blocks together imprecisely.

Bristle blocks come in a few basic shapes, the most numerous being $1\,^3/_4"$ × $1\,^3/_4"$ × $^1/_2"$ square tablets, of which there are many different colors available. There are also longer, flat tablets of a couple of different colors; and, finally, there are some flat discs and some flat right-angled triangle bricks.

The representation in **Figure 9** is the recommended product that the game should build. It is shown in more detail in **Figure 10**, including the detail of each brick's orientation in a translational position relative to one another. There are a couple of additional types of brick provided in the selection that have no purpose in the game except to add a little extra confusion, so they can be considered as obsolete materials not yet removed from stores.

The manufacturing process is detailed in **Figure 11**. There are four value-adding operations: the first puts the three square bricks together in the right order and orientation; the second adds the green disk to that subassembly; the third operation takes the yellow triangle and adds it to the

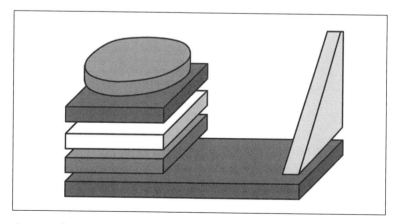

Figure 9. Simplified image of bristle block assembly.

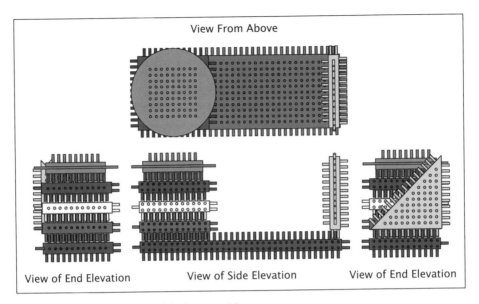

Figure 10. Detail of bristle block assembly.

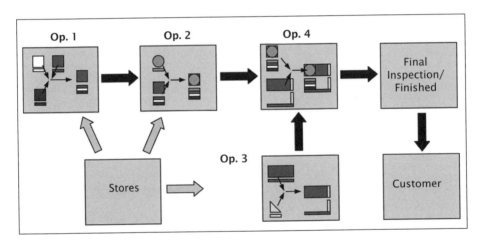

Figure 11. A depiction of the bristle block assembly process.

long red tablet; and the final operation takes the two assemblies and puts them together. One table, on which all the various bricks are kept, is used as the factory's stores, and one table is used as a final inspection workstation. The last of the seven tables is used to represent the customer's factory.

It takes two people to run this game: a Game Master, and a Facilitator. These two individuals will likely be selected as employees who are already ardent lean disciples. The Game Master is the main organizer for the training session, welcoming the participants, explaining why everyone has been chosen to take part, allocating each person to the particular role assigned to them, and setting down the rules of the game. The Facilitator works with the Game Master to ensure that everything runs smoothly, helping to make the performance measurements between each round of the game, and acting as the customer who knows exactly how to recognize what constitutes a conforming product. The Facilitator also acts as the timekeeper for the game, ensuring that each of the rounds can be fairly compared. All this will need to be carefully prepared for beforehand—it is a good idea for the Game Master and Facilitator to set up the training room and practice the game well in advance to avoid any unexpected or embarrassing problems.

Of the nine participants, two people are selected to be inspectors. One of these sits at the final inspection table (which also serves to store the finished product until it needs to be shipped to the customer), and the other is a roving inspector who can patrol up and down the four value-adding benches checking the work. Two people are selected to be forklift truck/lorry drivers; they are each supplied with a small tray (the lid of a shoebox, for example) to represent their forklift or lorry. These two people retrieve and carry raw material bristle blocks from the stores to the value-adding benches, and transport subassemblies from one operation to the next. One of them will intermittently need to act as a lorry driver, taking quality approved finished product to the customer when a call-off is made. The managing director's role (MD) is to observe the proceedings while each round of the game is running, and then help to generate improvement ideas to consider implementing between successive rounds.

It is advisable to make at least three of the four value-adding operators within the game key individuals, i.e., future change agents such as cell leaders, production engineers, production/shift managers, or a quality or materials manager. These people end up staying in the game longest and will benefit most from being operators. This role-reversal applies to the rest of the participants, too. Real life operators should be picked to be the MD and inspectors. Perhaps the roles of the two forklift/lorry drivers, who will soon be very busy in the game, should be filled by some administration staff who are used to being deskbound. At the beginning of the game, the seven small tables need to be spread around the room in an apparent random fashion, but in general the tables should make the initial round of the game as haphazard and confusing as possible, as seen in **Figure 12**.

There are four rounds of the game, each lasting five minutes. During each round, the customer, as played by the Facilitator, will place four orders with the factory. The customer states a predetermined order quantity, and the customer's factory gates remain open for 15 seconds following the order

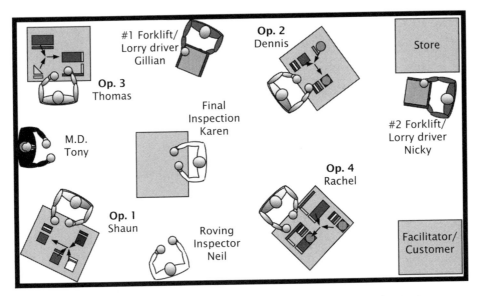

Figure 12. How to lay out the bristle block assembly process at the beginning.

to receive the required shipment. If the delivery arrives too late, it cannot be accepted and the "lorry" has to return the product to the factory. Any shortfalls in the delivery quantity compared to the amount ordered are carried over, and added to the next predetermined order quantity. The size of these orders varies between 6 and 18 units, but after each round the cumulative quantity of product that will have been requested by the customer will always come to a total of 46. In this way, the results at the end of each game can be fairly compared. This is explained to the players beforehand so that they know the game is being run fairly. To the players, the size of each order seems to be totally random and unpredictable, but in fact each order quantity will have been written on a planning sheet before the game starts.

After each round, 10 minutes is set aside to score how well the company did, and to allow the team to decide on *just two* improvement changes that they wish to make, and implement them before the next round commences in an effort to try to get the company into profit. It is the MD's responsibility to try to obtain consensus from the rest of the players as to which ideas to proceed with. He/she should also act as an observer who can walk around the "factory" during each game (without physically helping anyone) and make informed judgments about what is going wrong. Clearly, the basic goals will be to:

- eliminate the assembly of reject products
- greatly reduce levels of WIP

- reduce the amount of space (benches) being utilized

- remove nonvalue-adding operations.

One fixed rule is that the four value-adding operators as well as the MD cannot be removed from the game. The MD is an essential part of the business—someone who is needed to represent the business on behalf of the shareholders, and someone who will talk to the banks. It is possible for participants to suggest that anyone else may be removed from the game in order to reduce cost.

After four rounds have been completed, a supplemental fifth and final round is added. The Game Master sets out the one-piece-flow scenario that the team will not have been able to evolve into, even if they had thought of it in the time available to them. In this final round, the number of units ordered by the customer is increased from the usual 46 to 50. The players aren't told this until the summing-up at the end of the fifth game. This increased number helps to prove that JIT/kanban can perform far better than traditional methods. However, to keep things comparable, the calculations at the end are only based on 46 invoiceable units. A "random" order call-off pattern to use throughout the game would be:

	First Round	Second Round	Third Round	Fourth Round	Final Round
1st Order	10	15	7	9	15
2nd Order	8	14	16	14	12
3rd Order	16	6	10	7	8
4th Order	12	11	13	16	15

A whiteboard needs to be prepared (as below) prior to the training session to capture the details of the factory's performance during each round.

Game Turn:	First Round		Second Round		Third Round		Fourth Round		Fifth & Final Round	
	Order Size	Good Units Rec'd	Order Size	Good Units Rec'd	Order Size	Good Units Rec'd	Order Size	Good Units Rec'd	Order Size	Good Units Rec'd
GAME TOTALS										
Reject Units Received										
WIP $5 per brick										
AREA $250/table										
PEOPLE $200 each										
TOTAL COSTS										
INCOME $100/good unit										
PROFIT /LOSS										

In order to give the bristle block factory time to have a chance of keeping the customer supplied, the timing of the orders that the customer places throughout each round should be as shown in **Figure 13.**

In this way the factory personnel get a similar amount of information and time to respond as a real life factory would get, though in a greatly scaled-down manner.

The Facilitator needs to be checking the product he or she receives for conformance, because the customer will only pay the factory for good product. Invariably, during the early rounds, two things will happen: 1) the customer doesn't get sent a full delivery quantity, and 2) a great deal of the product that is shipped is rejected because the rotation or exact location of the bricks is wrong. Once the Facilitator knows, for example, that the order of 12 units has only met with a delivery of 10 units, 4 of which were reject, he or she first has to make the factory aware that only 6 good units have been received. Second, the shortfall needs to be added to the next order. To help the Facilitator keep track of this order delinquency situation, a prepared sheet is needed, see the example on the facing page.

Before the first round of the game begins, the Game Master and Facilitator show the four operators and the two inspectors how a good unit is fitted together without being told details about the orientation and translation complexity. They are allowed to study this for a while. In a later round, if it is one of the two suggestions the participants agree to implement, the Facilitator will provide samples of each subassembly or finished product to each of the operators and the final inspector to use as a quality standard. Invariably, these get mixed up in production and get shipped by mistake to the customer.

To begin with, the storemen have all the available bricks randomly heaped onto the store's bench. This disorder makes it take longer to get the

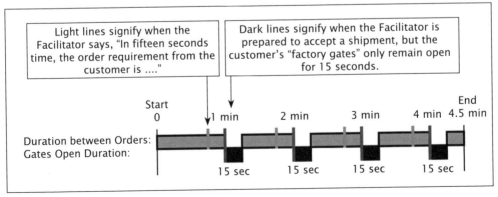

Figure 13. Pattern and timing of order placement and delivery points.

		Original Order Qty	Rolled Over Qty	Cumulative Qty Req'd	Good Units Rec'd	Order Shortfall
First Round	1st Order	10	-	10	4	6
	2nd Order	8	6	14	2	12
	3rd Order	16	12	28	0	28
	4th Order	12	28	40	0	40
					6 → ▼ 46	46
		Original Order Qty	Rolled Over Qty	Cumulative Qty Req'd	Good Units Rec'd	Order Shortfall
Second Round	1st Order	15	-	15	5	10
	2nd Order	14	10	24	3	21
	3rd Order	6	21	27	6	21
	4th Order	11	21	32	4	28
					18 → ▼ 46	46
		Original Order Qty	Rolled Over Qty	Cumulative Qty Req'd	Good Units Rec'd	Order Shortfall
Third Round	1st Order	7	-	7		
	2nd Order	16				
	3rd Order	10				
	4th Order	13				
						46
		Original Order Qty	Rolled Over Qty	Cumulative Qty Req'd	Good Units Rec'd	Order Shortfall
Fourth Round	1st Order	9	-	9		
	2nd Order	14				
	3rd Order	7				
	4th Order	16				
						46
		Original Order Qty	Rolled Over Qty	Cumulative Qty Req'd	Good Units Rec'd	Order Shortfall
Fifth (Kanban) Round	1st Order	15	-	15		
	2nd Order	12				
	3rd Order	8				
	4th Order	15				
						46

operators supplied with bricks. If they realize this and take time out to organize them by type, they will understand that there are a couple of types of bristle blocks that are not necessary in the pile. Removing these from the store helps to improve their game, and storing the other bricks in an organized manner will save them a great deal of time. Observe at what point this happens without drawing their attention to it. After the game, delivered product and rejects need to be broken down into individual bricks and returned to the stores by the Facilitator to prevent the game running out of components.

After the WIP has been counted at the end of each round, and the performance of the team has been scored on the whiteboard, the team is asked to face toward a flipchart and start suggesting possible improvements. The Game Master encourages the team to point out problems that they experienced, and the MD is tasked with noting them on the flipchart.

Typical propositions are to:

- reorganize the tables so everyone is in line and in the correct sequence
- ask for explanations as to exactly why some assemblies are rejects, and determine the differences between rejects and the conforming product
- have everyone inspect the assemblies they receive prior to using them
- turn one of the forklift drivers into an inspector
- get rid of one of the stores/forklift people and remove the roving inspector.

The Game Master should use judgement to persuade the team to ignore some suggestions if they are retrogressive, such as adding more value adders. Only two changes can be made in between each game: the team needs to agree which to choose from the list on the flipchart. If necessary, the MD should make the final decision.

After two or three rounds, new suggestions may be scarce. The Game Master may find it necessary to ask the team what additional information might make the factory's job easier, and tease out that more advance warning about order size would be helpful. The customer is asked if this would be possible and the Facilitator replies that it will be no problem. The next order requirement is announced at the start of the round and immediately after each delivery, giving the team 1 minute instead of 15 seconds for preparation.

In the fourth game, the team is allowed to implement three suggestions instead of the normal two, just to see how well the factory can perform. Before the fourth round, the Game Master may need to comment that many suppliers these days will deliver product right onto the shop floor without the need of an Incoming Goods facility. The team may then need yet further prompting to suggest, therefore, that they should do away with the stores and instead get "suppliers" to deliver lineside. Individuals that have been taken out of the game should be encouraged to volunteer to act as the bristle block suppliers, thereby resuming an active role in the game.

In the last game, the Game Master will give a demonstration of truly lean manufacture. The group is questioned about how much space is really needed to build the bristle block product. A paradigm blocks everyone's minds to the truth until the Game Master questions how many sides there are to a bench, and suggests that because there are four edges, four operators could all work at just one table.

A table is selected to perform the demonstration on, and a white sheet of laminate is placed on it and the four operators are then asked to gather round this one table. The first operator is asked to put his or her three blocks of "raw material" onto the laminate in an orientation and position that will optimize the building of his or her subassembly. After some trial assemblies, to prove that any unnecessary part orientation or excessive movements have been eliminated, some location/orientation marks are made around each bristle block with a colored marker pen to define precisely where the supplier of that particular brick will have to deliver them. A double or single line is used to describe the double or single rows of points down each side of the bristle block, thus exactly describing, as shown in **Figure 14**, the required workpiece orientation.

The downstream operator should be the one to determine (with occasional guidance from the Game Master) where he/she precisely requires the work to be placed for ease of assembly. The Game Master goes through the same

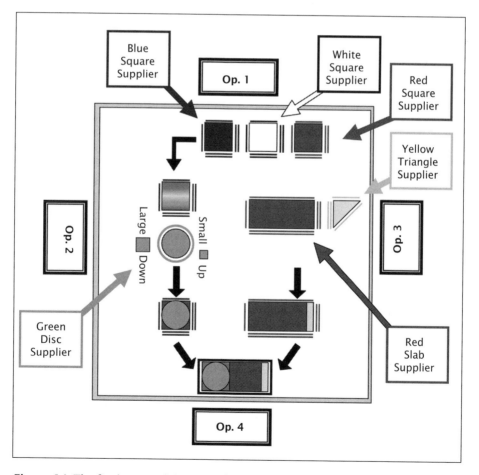

Figure 14. The final stage of the bristle block game—kanban and lineside delivery.

routine with each operator and the respective component/subassembly supplier. The laminated sheet ends up being a precise build instruction for the team that also defines exactly where lineside components are kept. The material suppliers are informed that they can only deliver a component if the "kanban footprint" where it is to be located is emptied by the action of an operator using up that brick. Each supplier is also instructed to ensure that he/she must deliver the bristle blocks preorientated exactly as specified by the operators.

Additionally, the factory is now moved right next to the customer, so that deliveries can be made much easier. The Game Master explains that new factories are often built right next door to the customer, especially in the case of automotive suppliers. This helps to strengthen the partnership bond and communication links between customer and supplier, and helps the two form a lasting sense of alliance. See **Figure 15**.

This final round needs 10 people to take an active part in the game—four operators and six component suppliers. This may, therefore, require the Game Master to get involved supplying one of the components.

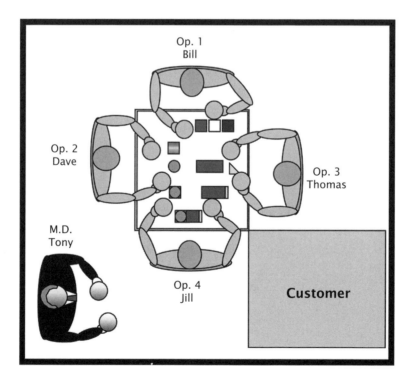

Figure 15. The final game layout.

Conclusion

The number of people and the space being utilized has now been cut to a minimum. With the component suppliers at the shoulders of each of the operators, the area can seem quite crowded. During the final game, the team works almost silently—this is in stark contrast to the first couple of rounds where there was chaotic shouting and running around. Nobody is panicking, nobody has to rush, everybody knows what they are doing. No rejects are produced and the team finds it easy to cope even with a maximum order quantity of 16 products to assemble within 1 minute.

After all five rounds of the game have been played, the factory's performance records will probably look something like this.

Game Turn:	First Round		Second Round		Third Round		Fourth Round		Fifth & Final Round	
	Order Size	Good Units Rec'd	Order Size	Good Units Rec'd	Order Size	Good Units Rec'd	Order Size	Good Units Rec'd	Order Size	Good Units Rec'd
GAME TOTALS	46	6	46	18	46	30	46	40	50	50 (46)
Reject Units Received	32		25		2		0		0	
WIP $5 per brick	60 $300		60 $300		60 $300		30 $150		10 $50	
AREA $250/table	6 $1500		5 $1250		4 $1000		3 $750		1 $250	
PEOPLE $200 each	9 $1800		8 $1600		7 $1400		6 $1200		5 $1000	
TOTAL COSTS	$3600		$3150		$2700		$2100		$1300	
INCOME $100/good unit	$600		$1800		$3000		$4000		$4600	
PROFIT /LOSS	-$3000		-$1350		$300		$1900		$3300	

At the end of the bristle block game, the Game Master must state categorically that although this game saw the number of "employees" decrease from nine people to just five, in practice the employer will not be making anyone redundant in the process of striving to become lean. In some cases, it will not be necessary to replace people who naturally leave through retirement or to work for someone else. It may be that some people's roles will change, but the growth in sales that lean will help generate will more likely guarantee existing jobs, and even increase employment levels compared to the company continuing to operate ineffectively and inefficiently by keeping to traditionally large batches.

Lean Games Conclusion

At the end of each of these three training games, take plenty of time to provide examples of instances in other companies where these new manufacturing principles are successfully being used. The individuals running these training games should have mentally prepared a way of summing up what lessons each of the games has taught. Additionally, there should be a clear and simple message that the company has already begun the journey toward becoming lean in order to maintain market position, and ensure job security for all the employees in the face of increasingly competitive times.

As with many games, all participants should be asked to keep the content of the games to themselves, as divulging the details will spoil it for anyone who has yet to participate in them.

Terms and Abbreviations Used in this Book

5-S: The full term is "5-S Housekeeping." There are five Japanese words, all beginning with "S," that describe the different stages of dramatically improving the housekeeping levels of a work area, from clearing out all the rubbish to making a world class working environment.

ATE: *Automatic Testing Equipment.* When a printed circuit board is fully assembled, it can be tested on an ATE that carries out an in-circuit and functional test. This checks that the components are present and are of the correct value, and also that key parts of the circuit are functioning properly. To do this, the pcb is pulled down with a vacuum onto a bed of golden contact pins (sometimes called a "bed of nails"). These make electrical connections to specific test-point pads on the pcb. Then the software in a computer performs each test in sequence before either passing or failing the board.

Book Value: Book value is an accounting term to describe the estimated worth of capital equipment or other assets during the course of its functioning life. This value will be depreciated each year, for example by a tenth of its total initial cost over the course of ten years, after which the accountant would state that it had a book value of zero.

Capital Equipment: Factory equipment is often referred to as "capital" equipment—capital being a way to describe the money invested or intended to be invested in equipment that is many thousands of dollars in value and will be useable for many years. Expensive tooling for such machines, though expensive, might have a much shorter useful life, and, therefore, would not be classified as being a capital expenditure.

CNC: *Computer Numerical Control.* This is a system in which a micro-computer or microprocessor is used as an integral part of how a piece of machinery is operated via a control panel. Different programs are written to perform different operations, making it a highly accurate and versatile way of machining components at relatively low cost. The term "CNC" is now synonymous with machining centers that utilize flexible tool changers; such equipment represents a considerable initial financial outlay to the business.

DFM: *Design for Manufacture* is achieved when a product is designed to perform all its required functions, but it is also designed to be very simple to assemble. This means that quality and mistake proofing are designed into the product, keeping reject rates to an exceptionally low level. It also means that the number of components is kept to an absolute minimum and the effort required to assemble the product is minimized.

EDI: *Electronic Data Interchange.* EDI is the name given to the transmission and receipt of structured data by the computer systems of trading partners. The data may be invoices, material requests, etc.

Faxbans: Faxbans are preprepared material requisition sheets that can be filled out by a supervisor with details of materials needed and then faxed off to the relevant supplier's company. These requisition sheets only allow materials to be ordered within specific quantity limitations (pack size and maximum amount) and are only filled out and sent on the specified day intended. If no materials need replenishing, then the faxban is sent with all the items showing a nil requirement. This is a simple way of empowering the people who ought to "own" the mundane task of repetitive material ordering to perform it without error, thereby reducing administration costs and increasing the performance of the cell's team.

FG: *Finished Goods.* The storage area at one end of the factory where packed and completed product is stockpiled prior to being shipped to customers.

FIFO: *First-in, First-out.* This is the normal method of stock rotation, using up the oldest materials first.

Fire Fighting: A term for the activity of rushing around correcting mistakes or problems, as opposed to preventing the problems from happening in the first place.

Golden Time: This is the absolute time it would take to perform a given operation, with no allowances for breaks, training, or suboptimum performance being included.

IT: *Information Technology.* IT makes use of computers networked together to run software that compiles information to determine what the business needs to be doing.

JIT: *Just in Time* is achieved when products or materials are made available just at the point when they will be required. JIT therefore promises the possibility of not needing to hold stocks of either raw materials or finished goods. To allow this to happen, customers need smaller and far more frequent deliveries from their suppliers. In some cases, the supplier builds a factory right next to his customer's factory to simplify the logistics of JIT. It is also known for the customer to charge the supplier with the cost of lost production if late delivery of materials results in his assembly line being stopped. The opposite of JIT is "just in case," where production for a shipment is planned early, and extra quantities are added to the batch to cover the possibility of some of the work later being found to be faulty.

Kaizen: A Japanese word that means "lots of small improvements." The principle behind kaizen is that operators have a great many ideas and suggestions that, although they might not be groundbreaking, are nonetheless probably relatively easy to implement and so numerous that they can collectively generate a large improvement. A byproduct of kaizen is that, when used well, it is very motivating for the team members because they have been able to make a significant contribution. Kaizen is in stark contrast to larger scale improvement projects that take months to implement, are organized by specialist engineers, and usually don't require much involvement from the work team.

Kanban: A Japanese word meaning "card" or "ticket." In manufacturing, kanban is a term used to describe a very simple build instruction, without which production for that item must not take place. Sometimes the trigger to begin building is for a card to be received, stating a specific requirement— there are a great many different ways for a kanban to be designed.

Lean Disciples: This describes those individuals who are both committed believers in Lean and who are also empowered change-agents within the organisation.

Lean Leap: This describes a method of "blitzing" a series of required actions into one focussed and intensive project in a quick and effective manner. In some circumstances, this is the best way to making lean implementations such as creating a "U"-shaped cell.

Louvered Panel: This is a steel sheet that has been stamped to produce a matrix of lugs across its surface so that, when mounted on a frame, it can be used to clip/mount plastic tubs or other holding arms/brackets onto itself. This is extremely useful for creating lineside material storage locations in a way that also promotes good housekeeping.

MDF: *Medium Density Fiberboard.* A term for a cheap composite wood-based board that is made from small fibers of wood glued together under pressure. It is cheap and easily cut, or shaped, using saws, drills, or routers.

MPS: *Master Production Schedule.* The MPS is a statement of what finished products need to be made, and when. It is based on the mix of products the sales forecast predicts, but it also considers the capacity limitations of the factory and work prioritization. This information is needed to drive an MRP computer system.

MRP: *Material Resource/Requirements Planning.* An approach to managing stocks and scheduling where demand can be planned or predicted, usually on the basis of the sales forecast. It is a computer algorithm commonly used in large manufacturing organizations that considers how long it takes to order components and then manufacture the work that is forecast. Its outputs are to state when the materials should be ordered, and when the factory will need to start building each of the subassemblies, etc., so that everything is ready at the right time.

MTO: *Make-to-Order.* When building a MTO product, the aim is to build the exact quantity and no more. This is a good technique for types of orders where it is undesirable to hold stocks of either WIP or FG because of expense and the intermittent nature of such orders.

PCB: *Printed Circuit Board.* A pcb is the modern way of creating a moderately complex electronic circuit. A sheet of nonconductive material, often called a "panel," has a layer (or sometimes many separate laminated layers) of copper tracks that are chemically etched in place. By connecting either SMT or conventional electronic components to the pcb panel, an electronic circuit can be assembled in a relatively short time.

Pull System: A system whereby materials are only replenished if they have been consumed, and the instruction or trigger to build something comes from downstream. In between discrete working areas there will be small amounts of WIP, often controlled by kanbans that are there to "prime" the production system for the next possible customer requirement.

Push System: A system where the initial processes in the factory are told to build components as part of a plan to make a mix of products that will be available to potential customers in many days time. The downstream operations are then advised what product to assemble using the WIP that eventually arrives in their area. In general, if some materials arrive, they must be needed, and therefore need to be processed and pushed on through to the next operation.

RBS: *Rate Based Scheduling*. This is a work scheduling tool that is good for stable, highly predictable, and repetitive customer demand for a particular product. It is where the building of a product is done at a constant rate each day, and it uses a limited amount of FG stock to act as a buffer against any small fluctuations in demand that might occur.

Runner: A term used to describe products whose sales requirements are both frequent and of large volume.

S&OP: *Sales and Operations Planning*. Where the sales forecast is discussed, and plans are made that will decide what the company will need to do to meet that sales demand, e.g., labor requirements, machinery capacity decisions, and the availability of materials.

Screamer: Screamers are those occasions where there is a very, very, urgent requirement for a particular type of material.

SMED: *Single Minute Exchange of Die*. This term relates to the changeovers on large machines; for example, molding machines or stamping presses. The tools that fit in these machines are sometimes called "dies." If a setup or changeover is closely studied, it is usually possible to reduce the time required to single figure minutes.

SMT: *Surface Mount Technology*. Most modern pcbs are partially assembled using surface mount machines to place the many tiny electronic devices onto the surface of the bare pcb. These "pick-and-place" machines are specialized robots with a gantry-mounted arm and camera that can pick up the components from the reels, trays, or sticks that they are stored inside. They have a computer program for each different pcb they may encounter, and each program defines the components required, their relative positions, and orientations. Preceding the "pick-and-place" machine is a screen printer for selectively applying solder paste to the board. After the components have been laid down, the SMT assembled pcbs go through a reflow oven that melts the solder paste and fixes the parts in place.

Spikes/Spikiness: Spikes are the sudden peaks in demand for material or product from the user. When there are spikes, there are also frequent periods of no demand, often known as "feast and famine." High degrees of spikiness within a demand pattern is a problem for lean manufacturing because, unchecked, it creates a need to have larger stockholdings. Reducing artificially created amplification of such demand fluctuations and then smoothing the demand pattern allows WIP to be reduced, and thereby workflow and effectiveness to be increased.

Stock-out: This is an occurrence where the customer runs out of a required part or product.

Stranger: A product that a customer requires on very few occasions.

Takt Time: Takt is a word that originates from the German word for "metronome." In manufacturing, it is used to calculate the correct size of a cell so that it has sufficient capacity to satisfy the requirements for materials by the next downstream user. Measured in seconds, it is the available daily or weekly working time divided by the number of units required in that period during the busiest period likely to be encountered. It is also used as a concept whereby the cell produces a single unit each takt period, i.e. a finished product pops out of the cell every 52 seconds in a regular and uniform way throughout the working day.

Visual Factory: A concept whereby all required information is available and on display. Imagine being able to go into any specific work area and being able to look at the display charts, noticeboards, and the cell itself, and being able to very quickly see what the cell does, how it has been performing, and what the problems are. Imagine how easy it would be to be trained to work in the cell if all the materials and tools were clearly identified and placed in dedicated locations, and the work instructions were also highly visual, making them easy to understand.

WIP: *Work in Progress.* WIP is materials that have already had some work done to them, but are not yet finished and at the moment are not being worked on. WIP is any material that is queuing, waiting its turn to be processed by a downstream operation.

Index